The BBC Micro ROM Book

Sideways ROMs and RAMs

Other books for BBC Micro users

The BBC Micro Machine Code Portfolio
Bruce Smith
0 246 12643 4

The BBC Micro Add-On Guide
Allan Scott, Mike Scott Rohan and Philip Gardner
0 00 383008 8

Introducing the BBC Micro
Ian Sinclair
0 00 383072 1

The BBC Micro: An Expert Guide
Mike James
0 246 12014 2

Discovering BBC Micro Machine Code
A. P. Stephenson
0 246 12160 2

Advanced Machine Code Techniques for the BBC Micro
A. P. Stephenson and D. J. Stephenson
0 246 12227 7

BBC Micro Graphics and Sound
Steve Money
0 246 12156 4

Practical Programs for the BBC Micro
Owen Bishop and Audrey Bishop
0 246 12405 9

Disk Systems for the BBC Micro
Ian Sinclair
0 246 12325 7

Advanced Programming for the BBC Micro
Mike James and S. M. Gee
0 00 383073 X

Take Off with the Electron and BBC Micro
Audrey Bishop and Owen Bishop
0 246 12356 7

Creative Animation and Graphics on the BBC Micro
Mike James
0 00 383007 1

Handbook of Procedures and Functions for the BBC Micro
Audrey Bishop and Owen Bishop
0 246 12415 6

The BBC Micro ROM Book

Sideways ROMs and RAMs

Bruce Smith

COLLINS
8 Grafton Street, London W1

Collins Professional and Technical Books
William Collins Sons & Co. Ltd
8 Grafton Street, London W1X 3LA

First published in Great Britain by
Collins Professional and Technical Books 1985

Distributed in the United States of America
by Sheridan House, Inc.

British Library Cataloguing in Publication Data
Smith, Bruce, *1955–*
    The BBC micro ROM book : sideways ROMs and RAMs.
    1. BBC Microcomputer—Programming
    I. Title
    001.64'24   QA76.8.B3/

ISBN 0-00-383075-6

Typeset by V & M Graphics Ltd, Aylesbury, Bucks
Printed and bound in Great Britain by
Mackays of Chatham, Kent

Also by Bruce Smith

The BBC Micro Machine Code Portfolio
75 Expert Routines

This outstanding collection of machine code routines and utilities sets
out – ready to use – what every user needs to\get the best from the
BBC Micro. Every program comes fully tested and includes a
demonstration call to show how it works and the type of application
possible.

0 246 12643 4

Contents

Acknowledgements		vi
Preface		vii
1	The ROM Paging System	1
2	Paged ROMs	13
3	Service ROMs	19
4	Language ROMs	33
5	The ROM Filing System	37
6	ROM Vectors	59
7	The TOOLKIT Interpreter	62
8	Breaking In	85
9	Home Brew	97
10	ROM and Board	145
11	Blow Your Own	163
12	BASIC Toolkits	178
13	Extra, Extra!	189
Appendix A: Converting BASIC I to BASIC II		203
Appendix B: ROM Book Programs in Bar Code Form		206
Appendix C: Useful Addresses		278
Index		280

Acknowledgements

Quite a few people have been involved in one way or another in producing this book and I hope I don't miss anyone out! First, a big thanks to all the manufacturers involved for supplying ROMs and boards on loan for me to play around with – Beebugsoft, Computer Concepts, Vine Micros, System Software, Mirco Pulse, Anderson Electronics, ISA Software, Aries Computers and Mirra Systems. I found the attitude of Beebugsoft extremely warming, in allowing me to reproduce details of the TOOLKIT interpreter which takes up the pages of Chapter 7. In these overpowering days of copyright protection it is nice to know there are still people around who are willing to share their expertise for the good of all. Particular thanks go to Adrian Calcraft of Beebugsoft and Mark Tilley, the author of TOOLKIT, for supplying answers to my many questions.

I am also indebted to Richard Mallett, author of ADDCOMM, for allowing me to reproduce details of the ADDCOMM operation and supplying the basis of the BRK interpreter as listed in Chapter 8.

I would ask you to support the manufacturers who have supported this book as these are people concerned with giving you a good service. Many were approached but not all responded and this might well reflect in their attitudes to you, the customer.

Other thanks go to 'me ole pal' Ray Harris for helping out on the hardware aspects of the book; Chris Drage for supplying photographs; and Jeremy Vine for something or other (satisfied?).

Finally, my thanks go to two of the nicest people I know, for help and valued advice whenever it's needed – Tony and Kitty at *Acorn User*.

Bruce Smith

Preface

The ROM paging system implemented on the BBC Micro is almost unique in home computing. The somewhat limited amount of memory available with the standard machine is in some ways compensated by the fact that up to sixteen ROMs containing machine code utilities and languages other than BASIC may be switched in and out of the BBC system at the keyboard and even from programs – effectively placing a further 240K at the programmer's fingertips!

At least 48K of this hidden memory is available to virtually every Beeb owner. The only requirement is that a series 1.0 operating system, or greater, should be present. Early Beeb owners who have the 0.1 OS present in the form of four EPROMs will need to have their machine updated to accept the new OS at a minimal cost by their local Acorn-approved dealer.

The aim of this – I think – rather unique book is not only to provide information on the ROM paging system but also to look at how the MOS handles it, how the different types of ROM software can be handled and written at home, and how to use, choose and handle all the ancillaries involved.

Chapter 1 explains how sideways ROMs are implemented and provides a useful reference detailing how the Beeb's case may be entered and ROMs handled and exchanged in an easy step-by-step operation. After dealing with the standard sideways ROM identification format, the two different types of sideways ROMs – languages and utilities – are examined in Chapters 2 and 3.

The ROM filing system is almost unknown to many people but it allows BASIC and machine code programs to be placed into a sideways ROM or RAM and downloaded into the computer memory as and when required, by using standard filing system commands. Chapter 5 provides full details and includes a formatting program to read files from disc or cassette and format them correctly.

ROM vectors and the use of extended vectors to enter sideways ROMs are examined in Chapter 6.

Understanding how an interpreter works is an important aspect of sideways ROM software development. Chapter 7 contains a detailed description of the TOOLKIT interpreter. TOOLKIT is a BASIC utility

ROM by Beebug and implements many of the functions that the sideways ROM/RAM programmers will need to understand.

Not all sideways ROM firmware is accessed via operating system commands. Errors may be trapped to 'catch' mistake errors. Chapter 8 looks into this and provides a suitable RAM-based program to add three extra commands to your Beeb's vocabulary.

Chapter 9 is one of the most practical. Its twelve programs provide suitable software to sit in ROM or sideways RAM, showing how utility type commands can be added as well as a simple language interpreter. The final four chapters look at the ancillaries involved, such as ROM extension boards, sideways RAM, EPROM programmers and erasers, BASIC toolkits, machine code monitors and various other utility ROMs. Included in these chapters are a couple of hardware projects to allow the user to build a multi-use sideways ROM extension box and an EPROM program with suitable software.

All the programs supplied are written using BASIC II. Most owners of older Beebs, however, will be using BASIC I. The main stumbling block for the latter users will be the use of the EQU functions in the assembler listings to assemble ASCII strings and bytes. To counteract this the Appendices contain suitable functions with examples, showing how these functions may be simulated in BASIC I.

Also included in the appendices are bar code listings. These allow readers who have the MEP bar code reader to read programs in from the pages of the book. Details of the bar code reader can be found with the bar code listings.

I have greatly enjoyed writing this book which, as I said at the beginning of this preface, is – I think – rather unique. As the saying goes, if you have half as much fun as I did then it certainly has been worthwhile.

One sobering thought that crosses my mind is that with this book I have probably passed my half-millionth printed word. Here's to the next half a million!

Bruce Smith
New Southgate
December, 1984

The BBC Micro ROM Book – The disc

You've read the book now get the disc – the programs from this book are available on 40 or 80 track disc for £7.95 (inc. VAT and p&p). Cheques or Postal Orders should be made payable to Lovebyte. Please state whether you require 40 or 80 track discs and send your order to:

Department JM
8 Grafton Street
London W1X 3LA

Chapter One
The ROM Paging System

In comparison with many of its contemporaries, the BBC Micro has a somewhat limited memory capacity. Like most home micros based on the reliable 6502 microprocessor it is quite capable of addressing a full 64K of memory. However, subtract 16K for the Machine Operating System (MOS), 16K for BASIC, another 3.5K for use by both of these and you're left with 29.5K of RAM. Fit a disc filing system and another 2.75K of RAM is eaten away. Use a high resolution graphics MODE and another 20K goes to display the screen. Actual memory to store programs and languages other than BASIC is now down to almost non-existent levels – perhaps just 6K if you are thrifty. This tightness was one of the first aspects of the Beeb's design to be investigated. Because of the sophistication and accessibility required for the MOS and the need for an almost super BASIC, it was essential to reserve a full 32K to house both the MOS and BASIC. Adding extra RAM to the memory map was possible, but expensive, requiring extra hardware and the software to handle it. The solution was to use the same area of memory several times, in banks of 16K, in parallel with the main memory

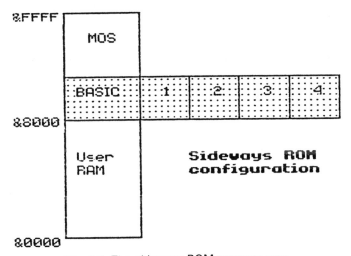

Fig. 1.1. The sideways ROM memory map.

map. A particular bank of memory could then be switched into this 16K slot when required, thus giving the ROM paging system.

Selecting the location for a bank of sideways ROMs was straightforward. The Beeb cannot operate without the MOS present; the area below the MOS, that holding the BASIC interpreter from &8000 to &BFFF, was ideal for storing the paging system. BASIC could be replaced with other languages that could be paged in its place by a special 'switch', while machine code utilities could be held in ROM and only paged in when they were required to perform a service.

The ROM filing system was also born. BASIC or machine code programs could be programmed into an EPROM and loaded directly into memory simply by selecting the ROM filing system and loading the desired program down. Figure 1.1 shows diagrammatically how the sideways ROM banks appear in the memory map, in relation to the overall plan of things.

Four!

The BBC Micro contains four sideways ROM sockets that are capable of holding ROMs that can be paged in and out of the Beeb's memory map. They are *not* capable of holding RAM.

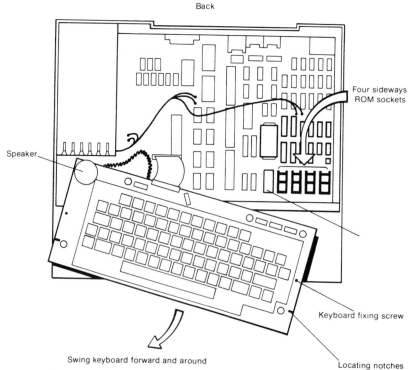

Fig. 1.2. Accessing the sideways ROM sockets (adapted from Acornsoft's ROM-fitting instructions, with permission).

The sideways ROM sockets, as they are generally known, are located in the lower right-hand side of the Beeb – under the keyboard, in fact, just to the right of the BREAK key (Fig. 1.2). Each socket is given a number which relates to its priority, or importance, within the Beeb. This priority is essential because, when you switch on, the MOS looks for a language to start up – or *boot up*, as it is generally termed. If several languages are present then the language it boots up will be the one located in the highest priority socket.

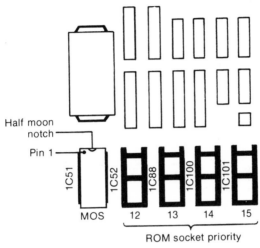

Fig. 1.3. ROM socket and IC numbers (adapted from Acornsoft's ROM-fitting instructions, with permission).

Figure 1.3 shows how the sockets are numbered on board. From outside, working in, we have socket numbers 15, 14, 13, and 12 with the MOS innermost. The right-hand socket, number 15, therefore has the highest priority and any language placed here will be booted up by the MOS regardless of what it is.

Other numbers are often given to these sockets – the IC number. This should not be confused with the ROM number. The IC number is the number assigned to that chip (IC=integrated circuit) in the overall plan of the Beeb. IC1 for example is the 6502 microprocessor. The IC number can be seen silk-screened in white on the board to one side of the socket. It is worth being familiar with these numbers (though not essential to know them by heart) as manufacturers' ROM-fitting instructions will often refer to them. Figure 1.3 illustrates these numbers and the associated sockets.

Under the bonnet

Gaining access to the sideways ROM sockets will be a necessity if you wish to use them to their full extent, so a familiarity with them and their physical whereabouts within the Beeb is most important. To do this it is necessary to open the Beeb up. If you are doing this for the first time then you will no doubt be apprehensive – but several excursions under the lid will relieve this (remember the first driving lesson?) and you'll soon become an old hand.

Warning

If your Beeb is still under guarantee then any tampering around inside will invalidate your guarantee rights.

To get at the sideways ROMs you will need a cross-point screwdriver, some room to manoeuvre and just a dash of confidence (no problem!). Step by step this is what you do:

(1) First switch off your micro and unplug it from the mains. It is also wise to turn off all devices connected to the Beeb, such as disc drives, printers and monitor or TV.

(2) Turn your micro upside down and locate the two screws marked 'FIX'. Remove these and place them somewhere safe (not on the floor!).

(3) Turn your Beeb the right way up but with the back towards you. You will see two similar fixing screws in the top two corners of the black plastic fascia sheets. Remove these and place them with the other two screws.

(4) Turn your Beeb around so that the keyboard is facing you and remove the lid of the Beeb by lifting it up from the edges. If you lean over your Beeb then you should be able to see the sideways ROM sockets on the right.

(5) The next step is to loosen the keyboard. Depending on which issue board you have there will be two or three nuts and bolts to remove. Place your hand under the Beeb at the front and lift the front up, so that the micro is almost on its 'hind legs' as it were. Locate the two or three cross point heads, within the black plastic fascia sheet, and loosen these so they are easy to turn. Place the Beeb flat and loosen the nuts the rest of the way by hand. Place the nuts and bolts plus shake-proof washers (if present) safely with the other screws.

(6) Take the keyboard in your two hands, one on each side, and lift it up a couple of centimetres and then pull it forward a few centimetres to expose the sideways sockets. You might need to turn the keyboard at an angle, slightly, to do this. The ribbon cable connecting the keyboard to the main board will be long enough to allow you to do this. If you have to disconnect this cable then you should have no trouble reconnecting it.

To reassemble the Beeb the above steps need to be repeated but in reverse. When it comes to positioning the keyboard you will notice that the board holding the keys has a small notch on each side about 4cm up from the bottom. It is important that these notches are located above the oblong raised mouldings on each side of the main case – thus ensuring that the keyboard is correctly positioned. Finally, when it comes to assembling the main lid, ensure that the three small red lights (LEDs) at the lower right-hand corner locate correctly in the corresponding three holes in the case itself.

Anatomy of a sideways ROM

The terms ROM and EPROM are applied freely to the chips that fit into the sideways ROM sockets and quite often the term ROM is applied when we really mean EPROM – perhaps because it sounds better. For the purpose of operation, there is really no difference between the two – you could not, for example, tell from the keyboard and screen whether the chip currently functioning is a ROM or EPROM.

Looking directly at the chip is another matter. An EPROM is clearly distinguishable by the fact that it has a 'window' in its top allowing you to see inside the chip and the silicon slice itself. A ROM is a totally enclosed black box (Fig. 1.4). ROM stands for *Read Only Memory*. EPROM stands for

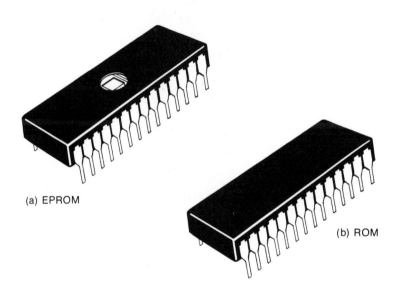

(a) EPROM

(b) ROM

Fig. 1.4. The difference between ROM and EPROM.

Erasable Programmable Read Only Memory. An EPROM can be erased and programmed over and over again many times, whereas a ROM can be programmed only once. From a home use point of view it is unlikely that you would ever become involved in programming ROMs, but EPROMs can be programmed using a Beeb and an EPROM Programmer. Programming ROMs is only a viable proposition if they are to be programmed in very large quantities as a special ROM mask has to be manufactured and this is costly.

ROMs and EPROMs to fit in the sideways ROM sockets have 28 pins or legs, 14 on each side of the chip. These pins are numbered from 1 to 28; pins 1 to 14 run down the left-hand side of the chip while pins 15 to 28 run up the right-hand side of the chip. The top of the chip is marked by a half-moon notch and pin 1 is directly to the left of this. The position of the half-moon notch is most important as this is used to orientate the ROM correctly prior to inserting it into a ROM socket. In addition to the half-moon and sometimes in place of it, pin 1 may often be identified by a small dot on the case next to the pin. Figure 1.5 shows the half-moon notch position and the numbering sequence of the pins.

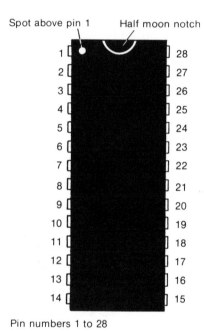

Fig. 1.5. Anatomy of a ROM.

Getting your priorities right

Before you insert any sideways ROMs into your Beeb there might be a need for you to rearrange the ROMs already present. As already mentioned, the language ROM in the highest priority socket will be the language the MOS boots up. If you wish to ensure that your Beeb always boots up BASIC when you switch on or press CTRL-BREAK then this chip should be inserted into the right-most sideways ROM socket – socket 15 and the IC 101 position.

Removing the BASIC ROM or any ROM from its socket is straightforward providing a number of precautions are followed. The ROMs themselves are manufactured using a technique called CMOS technology. It is not important to understand how this works but it is important to remember that they are susceptible to damage from static electricity. *Handling the ROMs, therefore, must take place only after you have earthed yourself to discharge any accumulated static electricity.* This can be done by touching any metallic surface that is itself earthed. There are certain surfaces that will act as accumulators and build up a static charge on your body. Nylon carpets are prime culprits so avoid working on these; the screens of monitors and TVs also accumulate such a charge so avoid contact with these too.

To remove a ROM you will need a small flat-bladed screwdriver. Following the above precautions, disassemble your Beeb's case as described above. Locate the chip you wish to remove and gently prize up each end using the flat-bladed screwdriver, a bit at a time as illustrated in Fig. 1.6. Once the chip is free, take care not to touch any of the silver 'legs' and lift it from the board using thumb and forefinger. Then place it on a clean surface away from any electrical devices such as transformers.

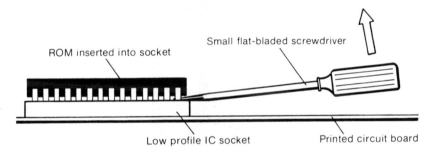

Fig. 1.6. Easing out the sideways ROM.

Back together again

Inserting a ROM into its socket requires care. The process should not be rushed and each stage should be double-checked. Follow these procedures step by step.

(1) Open your Beeb up and locate the sideways ROM sockets as described above, and decide which sideways socket you are going to use. If you need to reposition any ROMs remove them as already described.
(2) Earth yourself to discharge any static electricity.
(3) Before removing the ROM from its protective wrapper identify the half-moon or dot above pin 1.

(4) Remove the chip and hold it between thumb and forefinger and line it up over the ROM socket. Pin 1 and the half-moon notch should be pointing towards the back of the case.

(5) Now slowly apply firm pressure and push the pins into the corresponding receptacles of the socket, ensuring that all legs are located and are not splayed or bent.

(6) If the ROM is new, the legs may not line up correctly, sitting straddled across the socket. The pins will need to be bent inwards but *do not use your fingers!* Instead, choose a firm table surface and holding the chip at an angle press the pins along one length against the table, bending them in slightly (Fig. 1.7). Repeat this to the pins on the other side of the chip. The chip should now fit into the socket easily.

(7) Push the chip firmly home.

(8) Reassemble your Beeb and switch on to check if okay. Typing *HELP should display the ROM's name along with those of any other ROMs present.

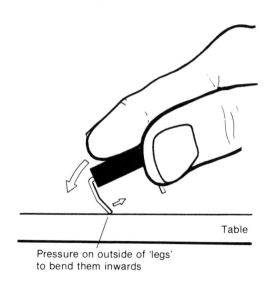

Pressure on outside of 'legs'
to bend them inwards

Fig. 1.7. Bending the legs using a table's edge.

A software switch

The switch that controls which of the sideways ROMs is paged in at any time is software-controlled. In fact, a particular ROM is selected by writing the binary representation of the ROM socket number into the low four bits of the Paged ROM Select Register at &FE30 – Sheila address &30.

There are several other bytes, within zero page RAM, that are associated with the ROM paging system, and these are detailed in Table 1.1.

Table 1.1. Paged ROM associated RAM addresses.

Address	Function
&F2–&F3	Text pointer vector
&F4	Value of currently selected ROM (copy of ROM Select Register)
&F6–&F7	Vectored address of current position in paged ROM

The vectored address at &F2 is used by the MOS as a text pointer for processing commands. Normally it will hold the address of the first character after the asterisk in the command, while the Y register holds the post-indirect index into the command.

The byte at &F4 simply contains a RAM copy of the currently selected paged ROM – a copy of the ROM Select Register.

Finally, the vectored address at &F6 holds the exact address of a position in a paged ROM.

Manipulating any of these addresses including the paged ROM selection register must be done from machine code. Poking them directly from BASIC or any other language will almost certainly result in the Beeb hanging up.

The coding required to select a particular sideways ROM is very simple. For example, to select the ROM in ROM socket 15, the coding would be as follows:

```
LDX #15       \   load X register with ROM number
STX &FE30     \   write to ROM select register
STX &F4       \   write RAM copy
```

Operating system read ROM call

Existing at &FFB9 is the operating system read byte from paged ROM call – OSRDRM for short. This call allows single bytes within paged ROMs to be read from machine code or from other paged ROMs. On entry, the Y register should contain the number of the ROM to be read, while the vector at &F6 holds the address of the byte to be read. On return from OSRDRM the accumulator contains the byte itself.

Program 1.1 illustrates how this call can be used to read the BASIC title string. The program begins by poking the address vector at &F6 with the

```
 10 REM Read Byte from a ROM
 20 REM Using OSRDRM           `
 30 REM (c) Bruce Smith
 40 REM The BBC Micro ROM Book
 50 :
 60 osrdrm=&FFB9
 70 osasci=&FFE3
 80 FOR pass=0 TO 3 STEP 3
 90 P%=&A00
100 [
110 OPT pass
120 .readrom
130 LDA #&80
140 STA &F7
150 LDA #8
160 STA &F6
170 .loop
180 LDY &F4
190 INC &F6
200 JSR osrdrm
210 BEQ out
220 JSR osasci
230 BNE loop
240 .out
250 RTS
260 ]
270 NEXT pass
280 CALL readrom
```

Program 1.1. Reading a byte from a paged ROM.

start address of the title string, &8008 (lines 130 to 160). The print 'loop' is entered at line 170. As we are entering the machine code from BASIC itself the ROM socket number of BASIC can be extracted directly from &F4 (line 180). The low byte of the address to be read is incremented (line 190), and the byte is read (line 200). A zero byte will indicate the end of the title string so this is tested for by line 210, otherwise the byte in the accumulator is printed and the loop re-executed (lines 220 to 230).

If you have several sideways ROMs present then their title strings can be printed simply by altering line 180. For example, if you have a ROM present in socket 14 then line 180 would become

LDY #14

By extending the main program loop, the contents of an entire ROM could be copied from ROM into RAM.

ROMBYTE

There are several OSBYTE calls associated with the sideways ROM system. These are detailed here, though it is not necessary to be totally familiar with them at this time. Table 1.2 lists the associated calls.

Table 1.2. OSBYTE calls associated with sideways ROMs.

OSBYTE		Function
&8D	(141)	Perform *ROM
&8E	(142)	Enter language ROM
&8F	(143)	Issue service request
&A8	(168)	Read address of ROM pointer table
&AA	(170)	Read address of ROM information table
&BA	(186)	Read number of ROM active at last BRK/error
&BB	(187)	Read number of socket holding BASIC ROM
&FC	(252)	Read/write current language ROM number

*OSBYTE &8D (*FX141)*
This call allows the *ROM filing system to be selected. There are no set up entry parameters and the accumulator contents are preserved. See Chapter 5 for full details of the ROM filing system.

*OSBYTE &8E (*FX142)*
This call will boot up a selected language ROM. On entry, the X register contains the socket number of the language to be entered. To enter another language from BASIC (if the language to be entered is in socket 14) then the syntax would be

   *FX142,14

Chapter 4 contains full details regarding language ROMs.

*OSBYTE &8F (*FX143)*
This call will cause the MOS to issue a paged ROM service request. Service requests are dealt with fully in Chapter 3. The entry parameters for this call are that the X register contains the service code and the Y register the service argument, if any. On exit the Y register may return a result if appropriate.

*OSBYTE &A8 (*FX168)*
This call returns the address of a ROM pointer table containing vectored addresses for entry into ROMs. This subject is dealt with in Chapter 6.
   On exit from the call, the index registers return the address of the pointer

table: low byte in X, high byte in Y. For the 1.2OS the address returned is &D9F.

OSBYTE &AA (*FX170)

This call returns the address of a ROM information table that contains details of types of sideways ROMs present in the Beeb. This information table is detailed in Chapter 2.

The address is returned in the index registers: low byte in X, high byte in Y. For the 1.2OS this address is &2A1.

OSBYTE &BA (*FX186)

This call returns the number of the ROM that was active when the last BRK error occurred. The value is returned in the X register.

OSBYTE &BB (*FX187)

This call reads the number of the ROM socket which contains the BASIC ROM. The number is returned in the X register. Chapter 9 contains details of its use to re-boot BASIC to exit from another language ROM.

OSBYTE &FC (*FX252)

This call returns with the number of the ROM socket containing the current language ROM in the X register. It is written to whenever a new langauge ROM is booted with OSBYTE &8E.

Chapter Two
Paged ROMs

To enable the Machine Operating System (MOS) to recognise a sideways ROM, the first couple of dozen bytes within the ROM (i.e. starting from &8000) must be arranged in a specific format. These bytes form what is known as the ROM header. When the Beeb is turned on or when a break is performed, the MOS scans through these header bytes to see whether a ROM is present in each socket and to ascertain what the ROM type is. Figure 2.1 details the format of the ROM header.

Offset	Designation
0	Language entry point
3	Service entry point
6	ROM type
7	Copyright offset pointer
8	Binary version number
9	ASCII title string
	Terminator byte, &00
	ASCII Version string
	Terminator byte, &00
	ASCII Copyright string
	Terminator byte, &00
	Tube relocation address

Fig. 2.1. Format of the ROM header.

The value under the heading offset indicates the number of bytes from the start of the ROM at which the specific item can be found. Thus, the ROM type has an offset of 6 and can therefore be found at &8000+6 or simply &8006. The first ten bytes of the ROM header are therefore fixed and may always be found at a specific address. The bytes that follow are important but may be of variable length. These bytes consist mainly of ASCII character strings that define the ROM title and copyright details. As is standard on the BBC Micro, each string is terminated by a zero byte, i.e. &00.

The copyright string, and in particular the C itself within the brackets, (C), is most important as without it the ROM will not be recognised as one! The byte at &8007 is the copyright string offset pointer; this byte contains the byte offset from the start of the ROM to the &00 byte immediately prior to the copyright string. During initialisation, the MOS extracts this value and uses it as an index to test for the presence of a copyright string. If there is one then the MOS is sure that a sideways ROM is present in that particular socket.

The next stage in the initialisation process is to build a ROM type table by extracting the type byte from each ROM and storing it in table form in block zero RAM for reference. The ROM type table in OS1.0 and OS1.2 is located from the sixteen bytes starting at &2A1. The address of the table can be read for other operating systems using OSBYTE 170. Entering and running the following program will return the start address of the ROM type table:

```
10 A%=170
20 X%=0
30 Y%=255
40 addr%=(USR(&FFF4)) and &FFFF00
50 addr%=addr% DIV 256
60 PRINT ~addr%
```

Table 2.1 details the addresses associated with each ROM in the ROM type table. The addresses are for OS1.0 and OS1.2.

Table 2.1. The ROM type table.

Table	ROM number
&2A1	0
&2A2	1
&2A3	2
&2A4	3
&2A5	4
&2A6	5
&2A7	6
&2A8	7
&2A9	8
&2AA	9
&2AB	10
&2AC	11
&2AD	12
&2AE	13
&2AF	14
&2B0	15

If any ROM sockets are found to be 'empty' then a zero is placed in the relevant table byte. Thus if ROM 8 were empty a zero byte would be placed at location &2A9.

After finding out what ROMs are present the MOS then polls each ROM in turn to determine certain factors from it, such as memory usage and so forth. These will be looked at shortly, but first let us examine each of the above sections of the ROM header in more detail.

Language entry point

These three bytes are used to hold a direct jump address which boots up the relative language. The first byte is always &4C, the opcode for JMP, followed by the two-byte JMP address.

Examples of ROM-based languages are BASIC itself, FORTH, LISP and BCPL. However, a ROM may still be classed as a language without being a language. Basically, the rule is that any program that is written such that it is independent of another language should be written as a language. Examples of this are machine code monitor ROMs such as Computer Concepts' GREMLIN or Beebug's EXMON.

A language is not entered through the language point directly from the MOS but via the service entry point. The only exception to this rule is BASIC which does not have a service entry point. If a ROM does not have a language entry point the language entry bytes should all contain zero.

Service entry point

All sideways ROMs must have a service entry point. The *only* exception to this is BASIC which is recognised as being BASIC by not having a service entry point. The first byte of the service entry point contains &4C, the opcode for JMP. This is followed by a two-byte address which points to the start of the service entry machine code polling.

ROM types

The byte at &8006 contains the ROM type. This provides the MOS with information about the ROM. The byte is organised at bit level as follows:

Bit 7: This bit is set if the ROM has a service entry, therefore it must always be set as all ROMs must have a service entry point. The *only* exception to this rule is BASIC.
Bit 6: This bit is set if the ROM has a language entry point.
Bit 5: This bit is set if the ROM has a second processor relocation address.

For this to happen the code in the ROM, bar the service entry coding, must have been assembled for the second processor addressing in mind. The service call coding is not copied across the Tube; only languages may be copied across the Tube.

Bit 4: This bit is used by ROMs operating on the Electron only. If set, it controls the use of soft key expansion allowing the Electron to implement function key operations using the CTRL and SHIFT sequences, as these are not normally available.

Bit 3: Not used – set to zero.

Bit 2: Not used – set to zero.

Bit 1: Must always be set.

Bit 0: Not used – set to zero.

The most common ROM type values are &C2 and &82. Examples of each are as follows:

&C2 = 1100 0010

This indicates that the ROM has both language and service entry points. ROMs with this type number include the following:

Communicator
EXMON
Multi-FORTH
View
Wordwise

The other main ROM type is

&82 = 1000 0010

This shows that this ROM has only a service entry. ROMs with this type number include the following:

ADDCOMM
DFS
Disc Doctor
Graphics Extension
TOOLKIT

The BASIC ROM has the type number:

&60 = 0110 0000

This indicates that it has a language entry point plus a Tube relocation address. As already mentioned, BASIC has no service entry point; bit 1 is also clear and this is normally set.

Copyright offset

As we have already seen, this byte at &8007 holds a byte which is the number of bytes from the start of the ROM to the &00 byte immediately before the copyright string. As described earlier, the copyright string is used to identify a paged ROM. In mnemonic terms, the following lines of code could be used to test for the presence of a ROM. The variable 'vector' is a zero page address vector containing &8000:

```
LDY #7            \   offset at +7
LDA (vector), Y   \   get offset
TAY               \   move into Y register
INY               \   add two
INY
LDA (vector), Y   \   get byte
CMP #ASC("C")     \   is it 'C' from (C)?
BNE norom         \   If no, there's no ROM!
```

Of course, according to Sod's Law, it could well be that if no ROM is present the byte of garbage being accessed could possibly be ASCII C. It is therefore worth testing the bytes on either side of the C to ensure that they are equal to ASC"(" and ASC")".

Version number

The version number is not used by the MOS at all. In fact, it is simply a byte provided for you to keep track of software development. The eight-bit value should relate to the version number of the software therein. Thus, if the software was version 5, the byte there might contain &05.

Title string

This is an ASCII string starting from &8009 and terminated by a zero byte. If the ROM is a language, the MOS prints this string when the ROM is initiated. This string is also normally the one printed out when *HELP is executed.

Version string

This ASCII string is entirely optional. It allows the user to print the version number of the ROM during the processing of *HELP. This string must be terminated by a zero byte, &00. If the ROM is a language then on entry to it the error pointer vector at &FD and &FE will be made to point to the version number if it is present. If the version string is not present the error pointer will point to the copyright string.

Tube relocation address

If bit 5 of the ROM type byte is set then the MOS expects to find a Tube relocation address at this point. This is the address to which the ROM contents, which will be a language, would be copied. The code must therefore be written with the second processor relocation address borne in mind. The service coding should not be written in this way, but assembled as normal. This is because the service code is not copied across the Tube.

Chapter Three
Service ROMs

All paged ROMs, with the exception of BASIC, must have a service entry point. The machine code here will depend on the sophistication of the ROM. Generally, it must be capable of handling all the calls sent to it by the MOS and must include the interpreter that allows the ROM to identify and execute commands that are based within it. In all there are twenty-one possible service calls though most will not require processing by service-only ROMs.

When a service call is made, the highest priority ROM is polled first, and the call is then passed down through the ROMs until a ROM recognises the service call and proceeds as required. When a service entry is required, the three processor registers are used to pass the service call details as set out in Table 3.1.

Table 3.1. Service call register initialisation.

Register	Contents
Accumulator	Service type
X register	Number of current ROM
Y register	Any extra service parameter

If the service call is not recognised by the current ROM the service coding must restore all register values and return with a simple RTS instruction. Though generally it will normally be the MOS issuing the service call, other ROMs may also issue a service call using an OSBYTE call as follows:

```
LDA #&8F        \   issue ROM service call
LDX #type       \   X contains service type requested
LDY #param      \   Y contains any parameter
JSR OSBYTE      \   and execute
```

On return from the OSBYTE call, the Y register will contain any resultant value so this should be checked as required.

Table 3.2 lists all the service call types which will be discussed below.

Chapter 9 provides suitable coding examples showing how many of these service call types can be implemented and processed.

Table 3.2. Service call types.

Call type	Description
0	Call already provided
1	Claim absolute workspace
2	Claim private workspace
3	ROM auto boot
4	Command not recognised
5	Interrupt not recognised
6	BRK
7	OSBYTE unrecognised
8	OSWORD unrecognised
9	*HELP
10	Claim static workspace
11	Release NMI
12	Claim NMI
13	Initialise ROM filing system
14	Return byte from ROM filing system
15	Vectors claimed
16	EXEC/SPOOL files about to close
17	Character set about to explode/implode
254	Secondary Tube initialisation
255	Main Tube initialisation.

Service call 0

This is not really a call as such, but rather a signal to the MOS and other ROMs that the original service call has been recognised and processed. If a ROM recognises a service call after processing it, then it should place zero into the accumulator before executing the final RTS.

Assuming that the original service call type has been pushed onto the stack, the coding is simply:

```
PLA        \ pull stack to balance previous push
LDA #0     \ load call recognised code into accumulator
RTS        \ and return to calling MOS or ROM
```

Service call 1

This service call is issued on power up or break. Its purpose is to determine the total amount of shared workspace required by paged ROMs. For example, a DFS often requires up to 2.75K of memory workspace to function. Thus, the normal value of PAGE is incremented from &E00 to around &1900.

When this service call is issued, the Y register contains the page number of the present upper limit of this absolute workspace. This value should be checked by a ROM requiring workspace. If the value is less than that required then the value of the Y register should be incremented until there is sufficient memory. Generally, if a DFS is fitted, the 2.75K this normally claims will usually be enough for most ROMs. On tape-based systems where PAGE is normally &E00, the need for extra workspace is likely to occur. For example, Computer Concepts' Graphics Extension ROM requires 256 bytes of workspace, so if this is fitted on a tape-based system then PAGE will be set to &F00 by this ROM.

As an example, consider that a ROM you are writing requires two pages of RAM for workspace. The coding to check and implement this might look like this:

```
CMP #1          \  was it absolute claim?
BNE next        \  branch if not
CPY #&10        \  is it >= &E00+&200?
BCC no          \  branch if needs incrementing
RTS             \  all okay so return
.no
CPY #&0E        \  is it +1 or +2?
BNE one         \  branch if only one page
INY             \  increment page value
.one
INY             \  increment page value
RTS             \  and return.
```

It is vitally important that the value in the Y register is *not* decremented, because this would eventually lead to totally corrupted programs that even a suitable Bad Program cure will be unable to solve. You have been warned!

Service call 2

This call is issued after service call 1 has been completed. It allows ROMs to claim their very own private workspace area above the absolute workspace area, as illustrated in Fig. 3.1. This area of memory is exclusive to the ROM claiming it and may not be used by other ROMs. This means that the ROM

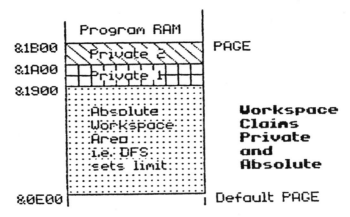

Fig. 3.1. Private and absolute workspace configuration.

may store important data in its own private workspace area without fear of corruption.

On issuing the service call, the Y register contains the value of the first free page. If the ROM requires some private workspace it must save the current contents of the Y register in a special ROM workspace table that runs from &DF0. Table 3.3 details the byte associated with each ROM.

Table 3.3. The ROM workspace table.

ROM number	Table byte
0	&DF0
1	&DF1
2	&DF2
3	&DF3
4	&DF4
5	&DF5
6	&DF6
7	&DF7
8	&DF8
9	&DF9
10	&DFA
11	&DFB
12	&DFC
13	&DFD
14	&DFE
15	&DFF

ROM 6 would therefore place the Y register contents at &DF6. This value is the start address of the private workspace table. The contents of the Y register can then be incremented the desired amount to make space for the current ROM's private area before the 'new' base value is passed back to the MOS. For example, if the ROM requires 180 bytes of private workspace the contents of the Y register must be incremented by one, thus reserving a total of 256 bytes of private workspace, the minimum possible.

The following coding shows how a page of private workspace can be claimed:

```
CMP #2          \  is it private workspace claim?
BNE next        \  if not branch over code to next test
TYA             \  move base into accumulator
STA &DF0,X      \  save start of private workspace
INY             \  need one page
LDA #0          \  indicate call serviced
RTS             \  and return without corrupting registers
```

The above example assumes that the X register has not been corrupted and contains the current ROM number and, therefore, the correct index into the workspace table.

Whenever the private workspace is needed its start address can be obtained from the table and used with indirect addressing as required. It is important that any code written does not corrupt this table. The following example shows how the zero page user RAM could be saved at the start of the private workspace area.

```
LDX &F4         \  get ROM number
LDA &DF0,X      \  get start page
STA vector+1    \  place in high byte of vector
LDA #0          \  clear accumulator
STA vector      \  and save in low byte of vector
LDY #32         \  32 bytes to save
.loop
LDA &70,Y       \  get byte
STA (vector),Y  \  save in private workspace
DEY             \  decrement index
BPL loop        \  do next byte until Y is negative
```

Service call 3

A ROM may be auto-booted at break if so desired. This service call is issued after a BREAK, and in conjunction with a key. For example, a ROM could be made to implement a HELP on BREAK if the H key is pressed at the same time. On receiving this call, the ROM should proceed by examining the keyboard. If the correct key is detected, the routine can place the ASCII string *HELP into the keyboard buffer using OSBYTE &8A. A typical coding for this might proceed along the following lines:

```
CMP #3              \  was it BOOT?
BNE next            \  if not branch to next
LDA #&7A            \  perform a keyboard scan
JSR OSBYTE          \  any key pressed returned in X
CPX #&54            \  was it internal key code for H?
BNE notme           \  if not branch to notme and restore registers
LDA #&0F            \  flush all buffers
JSR OSBYTE
LDA #&8A            \  insert value into buffer call
LDX #0              \  specify keyboard buffer
LDY #ASC("*")       \  and write "*HELP"
JSR OSBYTE
LDY #ASC("H")
JSR OSBYTE
LDY #ASC(".")       \  use short form
JSR OSBYTE
LDY #13             \  don't forget RETURN
JSR OSBYTE
RTS                 \  and return
```

The key D should not be used as this is reserved to boot any DFS into existence should it not be implemented as the default filing system.

Service call 4

This is the call issued by the operating system when it encounters an operating system call that it does not recognise. An operating system call is simply a command prefixed with an asterisk, e.g. *SAVE is an operating system command. Generally, commands implemented in sideways ROM utilities will be implemented this way. The unrecognised command is first offered to the sideways ROMs and then, if not recognised, to the currently active filing system.

When this service call is issued, the bytes at &F2 and &F3 hold a vectored address pointing to the unrecognised command that is in the form of an ASCII string terminated by a RETURN character, ASCII 13. The Y register should be used to access post-indirectly each byte in the string. This register is already set up on entry to point past any leading spaces and the asterisk, so its value must be preserved in case the command is not recognised by the current ROM. Chapter 9 contains full details on interpreting and executing unrecognised commands. Once a command has been recognised and executed the accumulator should be set to zero to indicate to the MOS or calling ROM that the command has been processed.

Service call 5

This call is issued by the MOS when an interrupt request (IRQ) that it does not recognise has occurred. If your paged ROM makes use of the IRQ line then it should be directed to the suitable interrupt request polling routine and any devices checked to see if they are the source of the IRQ. If the ROM recognises the interrupt after processing it, it should set the accumulator to zero to indicate that the interrupt has been serviced and then return with an RTS instruction and *not* and RTI as is generally the norm in this instance. The following coding shows how a suitable pooling routine might be instigated:

```
CMP #5          \  is it unrecognised IRQ?
BNE next        \  branch to next test if not
JSR polling     \  execute IRQ polling
BCC notfound    \  carry clear if IRQ not identified
PLA             \  pull stack to balance previous push
LDA #0          \  call serviced
RTS             \  return
.notfound
PLA             \  put service code in accumulator
RTS             \  and return
```

As usual, this coding assumes that on entry the service call type was preserved on the stack.

If an IRQ is not identified by any of the paged ROM firmware then the MOS directs a final call through the user vector IRQ2.

Service call 6

This service call is used to inform paged ROMs that a BRK has occurred, before the MOS hands control over to the current language ROM, via the BRK vector, BRKV, to process the BRK. In many instances, the BRK is used to signal an error, and printing of an error message. If the service call does not intend to process the BRK – for example, to produce some extra fancy error messages and pointers – the contents of all registers should be preserved. The vectored address at &FD and &FE points to the error number in memory while the byte at &F0 contains the value of the hardware stack pointer after the BRK was executed. As the BRK may have occurred in ROM other than the current ROM processing the BRK, it is important to be able to ascertain just which ROM it did occur in. To do this, OSBYTE &BA should be called; the ROM number is returned in the X Register.

Service call 7

This call effectively allows the user to implement his own OSBYTE calls as it is issued by the MOS when it does not recognise an OSBYTE call. Three locations in zero page hold the OSBYTE parameters when this service call is issued. The locations and their use are as follows:

&EF   Accumulator
&F0   X Register
&F1   Y Register

The new OSBYTE coding should therefore check the contents of &EF to determine whether the OSBYTE is implemented by the ROM servicing the call.

On the 1.2 OS the following OSBYTE call codes are unassigned:

OSBYTE &15 to &74 inclusive
OSBYTE &A1 to &A5 inclusive

An OSBYTE &A1 could be implemented in sideways ROM using the following coding:

```
CMP #7        \   was it OSBYTE?
BNE next      \   branch to next if not
LDA &EF       \   get OSBYTE code
CMP #&A1      \   is it this ROM's OSBYTE call?
BEQ yes       \   branch to yes if it was
PLA           \   else restore previously pushed code
RTS           \   and return
.yes
LDX &F0       \   get X parameter
LDY &F1       \   get Y parameter
    :         \   OSBYTE functioning coding here
    :
PLA           \   all done so restore push
LDA #0        \   indicate call serviced
LDX xval      \   get new X return value
STX &F0       \   write to X byte
LDY yval      \   get new Y value
STY &F1       \   write to Y byte
RTS           \   and return
```

If the call is processed by the ROM in addition to returning with the accumulator clear, the X and Y registers' values should be returned to the MOS in their respective bytes at &F0 and &F1 as well as in the index registers. Failure to do this will result in incorrect values being inserted into the index registers by the MOS on completion.

Service call 8

This call is issued when an unrecognised OSWORD call is performed. As with the previous service call, this allows the user to implement his own OSWORD procedures. The registers are stored in zero page as follows:

Accumulator	&EF
X Register	&F0
Y Register	&F1

The contents of &EF should be checked for a valid OSWORD by the service coding and locations &F0 and &F1 will contain the parameter block address. The following OSWORD call numbers are not used by the 1.2 OS:

OSWORD &0E to &CF

OSWORD calls of &E0 and greater are sent directly to the User Vector, USRV at &200, and thus should not be used for implementing ROM-based OSWORD routines.

The following code shows how this service call may be detected for OSWORD &22:

```
CMP #8          \  is it unknown OSWORD?
BNE next        \  branch to next if not
LDA &EF         \  get OSWORD code
CMP #&22        \  is it &22?
BNE no          \  branch if not
JSR dosword     \  perform operation
PLA             \  pull previously pushed code
LDA #0          \  signal processed call
RTS             \  and return
.no
PLA             \  get service call 8 back
RTS             \  and return to test next ROM
```

As the index registers are stored in zero page in standard 6502 form, low byte first, they can be used in combination with the Y register as a vector to allow access to the parameter block using post indirect addressing. For example, the first byte in the parameter block could be loaded into the accumulator with:

```
LDY #0          \  clear indexing register
LDA (&F0),Y     \  and get first byte
```

Service call 9

This is the *HELP service call to which all ROMs should respond at once. The locations at &F2 and &F3 form a vectored address to which the Y register acts as an index to point just beyond the *HELP command. Each ROM should save the Y register and then check for any further *HELP parameters in the line and respond accordingly if it recognises any of them. If not, the Y register should be restored and no further action taken by the ROM. If the line is just a simple *HELP followed by ASCII return then the ROM should produce its standard *HELP message.

The following coding is a simple *HELP implementation that responds with

    GRAPHICS V1.23
        circle
        ellipse
        square

when required to do so.

```
        CMP #9              \   is it *HELP?
        BNE next            \   branch if not
        TYA                 \   move index across
        PHA                 \   and save on stack
.getbyte
        LDA (&F2),Y         \   get next byte
        CMP #&20            \   is it space
        BNE over            \   branch over if not
        INY                 \   move to next byte
        BNE getbyte         \   and test next byte
.over
        CMP #&0D            \   is it ASCII return?
        BNE notsimple       \   branch elsewhere if not simple *HELP
        LDY #&FF            \   initialise index
        LDA #hitable        \   get high byte address
        STA vector+1        \   of table and save
        LDA #lotable        \   get low byte address
        STA vector          \   of table and save
.loop
        INY                 \   increment index
        LDA (vector),Y      \   get ASCII byte
        JSR OSASCI          \   print it
        BNE loop            \   branch for next byte if <>0
        PLA                 \   pull Y register
        TAY                 \   and restore index
        PLA                 \   restore service call
        RTS                 \   and return
.table
        EQUS "GRAPHICS V1.23"
        EQUB &0D
```

```
EQUD &20202020
EQUS "circle"
EQUB &0D
EQUD &20202020
EQUS "ellipse"
EQUB &0D
EQUD &20202020
EQUS "square"
EQUD &0D0D
EQUB 0
```

After a *HELP call, the accumulator should return with the service call number, 9, in it so that other ROMs may respond to the *HELP command.

Service call 10

This service call should be issued by a ROM when it wishes to use the main workspace from &E00 onwards, which was originally defined using service call 1 at Break. To initiate this call the ROM must execute the following OSBYTE call:

```
LDA #143
LDX #10
LDY #255
JSR OSBYTE
```

On receiving service call 10, if the ROM is using the main workspace it should copy any valuable information to its private workspace should it have claimed any on a break initialisation. It is a good idea to keep a flag within your own private workspace to indicate whether you are in control of the main workspace area at any time. When the main workspace has been claimed by a ROM it is also free to use zero page workspace from &B0 to &CF inclusive.

Service call 11

The major filing and networking systems on the BBC Micro make extensive use of non-maskable interrupts (NMIs). This call should be used when the ROM system currently using it no longer needs to do so and is prepared to release it. When this service call is issued, the Y register holds the number of the ROM that had previously used the NMIs before the claim for them was made. Each ROM that recognises this call should check the contents of the Y register with its own ROM number, which is available in the X register and location &F4 at the time of the service. If it is the same then the accumulator should hold zero on return from the service call otherwise all registers should be preserved.

The following coding shows the general procedure for handling this call if the ROM is making use of the NMIs.

```
CMP #12      \  is it NMI release?
BNE next     \  branch to next if not
TYA          \  move last ROM number into accumulator
CMP &F4      \  is it this ROM?
BNE notme    \  branch if not
PLA          \  balance previous push
LDA #0       \  recognised code
RTS          \  and return
.notme
PLA          \  restore service call number
RTS          \  and return
```

To return the use of the NMI to its previous user, OSBYTE 143 should be executed as follows:

```
LDA #143     \  OSBYTE code
LDX #11      \  service call code
LDY #255
JSR OSBYTE   \  issue request
```

As mentioned, this service call will normally only be used if the user is implementing a filing system. Care must be taken when using NMIs as the Beeb is interrupt-driven and funny things can happen to general house-keeping chores if they are not treated properly. Note also that the zero page locations associated with the filing system should not be used during this service call's execution.

Service call 12

This call is issued to claim use of the NMIs. It is initiated with OSBYTE 143 as follows:

```
LDA #143     \  OSBYTE code
LDX #12      \  service call 12
LDY #255
JSR OSBYTE   \  perform call
```

The ROM that currently has claim of the NMIs should place its ROM number into the Y register and store any important data in its own private storage area. In addition, it should also inhibit any further use of NMIs until it has reclaimed the NMI at a later stage. The claiming ROM should also store the ROM number of the current NMI for use when releasing the NMI claim. If the ROM was not using the NMIs then the Y register must remain unaltered. Once claimed, the zero page area associated with NMI handling from &A0 to &A7 is free for use and the ROM's resident NMI service routine should be copied to &D00.

Service calls 13 and 14

These service calls are issued in reference to the *ROM filing system and are discussed fully in Chapter 5 which details the ROM filing system.

Service call 15

Whenever a new filing system is initialised it must perform a number of operations. One such operation is to repoint all vectors into the coding of the new filing system. After writing relevant addresses into the various filing system vectors, this service call should be issued by the new filing system to inform all other paged ROMs that a change in filing system has occurred.

Service call 16

This call is performed to inform paged ROMs that may be using SPOOL or EXEC files that a filing system change is being performed. On receiving this call, any ROM using such files should perform any required housekeeping to tidy things up. If a ROM requires the SPOOL or EXEC file to remain open, then a zero should be placed into the accumulator prior to releasing the service call.

Service call 17

This call is issued when the character font, i.e. the user-definable character set, is about to explode or implode. In the first instance, this will result in the MOS claiming more memory space, thereby moving the Operating System High Water Mark (OSHWM) up the memory map. The value assigned to PAGE will therefore increase. In the later case, the extended character set will not be required and the level of the OSHWM will be decreased resulting in the value of PAGE being lowered. This service call is implemented when the MOS encounters an OSBYTE &15 (*FX20) call. On encountering the call, the ROM should move any data liable to be corrupted out of harm's way.

Service call 18

This call is provided to allow filing systems to be initialised without having to issue any operating system commands. This is important as a program may need to have files open in two or more filing systems. The filing system should check the contents of the Y register to see if it is the same as its operating system filing system code as defined by OSARGS. If the ROM is identified as the called filing system, it should initialise itself and restore all the files that were open during the time it was previously shut down.

Service call 254

If the Tube interface is present, this service call is issued after OSHWM has been defined, thus allowing the Tube firmware to explode the character font or reserve memory as required.

Service call 255

This call is issued if a Tube interface is detected and is used to initialise the main Tube system. It is issued prior to the final setting of the OSHWM, allowing memory to be arranged and start-up messages printed.

Chapter Four
Language ROMs

The first three bytes of a paged ROM are referred to as its *language entry point*. The first byte will normally contain the JMP opcode, &4C, followed by the two-byte address of the beginning of the language coding. If the ROM is a service ROM only, these three bytes should all contain zero bytes.

The BBC Micro must always have at least one language present for it to be able to function correctly, otherwise it will cause the MOS to hang up after issuing the error message, 'Language?'. The default language will be the one in the highest priority sideways ROM socket. Normally this will be BASIC but there is no reason why it should not be a word processor or machine code monitor.

The normal way in which a language is entered is to type in a command that the ROM will recognise. For this purpose all language ROMs must contain a service entry point, to an interpreter that will attempt to recognise the command. The command *FORTH, for instance, might be used to select a FORTH language ROM. The service entry interpreter must be capable of recognising this command and then select itself as the new language ROM. To do this the ROM must issue OSBYTE &8E, with the X register containing the ROM number. It is important to remember that this OSBYTE call never returns as it re-enters the ROM through its language entry point, resetting the stack and registers *en route*. Consequently, there is no real need to preserve registers as they are destroyed anyway! The coding to perform the language entry is simply:

```
LDA #&8E
JSR &FFF4
```

The X register should already hold the ROM identity though this can always be extracted from &F4 should it have been destroyed. To start up the selected language, the MOS notes the number of the ROM so that it can reselect the language ROM when a soft break is performed. Then the MOS displays the ROM title string to indicate that the particular language is in use. The error message vector is pointed towards the copyright message or version string if it is present, whereupon the language point is entered with the accumulator containing 1 to indicate a normal start up.

Once a language has been initialised, it has 1024 bytes of workspace free for private use running in a single block from &400 to &800 in addition to the zero page locations normally associated with a language ROM between &00 to &8F. The language program space exists between the Operating System High Water Mark (OSHWM) and the bottom of the currently selected screen mode.

Language ROMs may also be entered by two other methods. The first method is by issuing an *FX 142 call. This call must be post-fixed by a number which relates to the ROM socket number containing the language to be switched in. Thus, to select the language in ROM socket number 12 the command

   *FX 142, 12

will suffice.

The second method of entering a language is to auto-boot it by pressing the BREAK key in combination with another specific key. To do this the service interpreter must trap the auto-boot service call, 3, issued by the MOS on BREAK, and test for its particular auto-boot key. For example, we might wish our imaginary FORTH ROM to be selected by BREAK-F, i.e. when the BREAK and F keys are pressed together. Suitable coding to perform this is as follows:

```
CMP #3              \  is it auto-boot service?
BEQ autoboot        \  branch if it is
PLA                 \  restore service type
RTS                 \  return somewhere
.autoboot
LDA #&7A            \  perform keyboard scan
JSR &FFF4
CPX #&43            \  was it internal "F"?
BNE somewhere       \  branch if not
LDA #&78            \  write key information
JSR &FFF4
LDA #&0F            \  flush buffer of any other keys
JSR &FFF4
LDA #&84            \  select entry to language
LDX &F4             \  get ROM id
JSR &FFF4           \  and implement language
```

The only thing to remember here is that the keytest is performed using internal key numbers. Figure 9.5 (see page 129) contains a list of these.

Absolute musts

There are three things a language must do; if not, it simply will not function correctly and will cause the machine to 'hang up'. First, interrupt requests must be enabled for the MOS to continue to work correctly; a simple CLI will perform this. Second, the BRK vector, BRKV at &202, must also be set ready to handle errors as they occur. All language ROMs must include error handling facilities, as even the simplest of tasks, such as an OSWRCH call, can generate an error. Finally, the stack pointer will be undefined so this should be reinitialised. These three tasks require a minimum of code as the following short listing demonstrates:

```
CLI                        \   enable IRQs
LDX #&FF                   \   reset stack pointer
TXS
LDA #brkhandle MOD 256     \   get low byte error handling entry
STA &202                   \   store low byte BRKV
LDA #brkhandle DIV 256     \   get high byte of same
STA &203                   \   and poke into BRKV high byte
```

On entering a language, the accumulator will contain a language entry code. Normally these can be ignored though two will be of interest if the language ROM is to be Electron compatible. The four entry codes are as follows:

Accumulator=0
There is no language present and the Tube ROM is being called. This call must not be intercepted other than by the Tube ROM itself.
Accumulator=1
Normal entry to language.
Accumulator=2
Request next byte of soft key expansion. The key number is set by issuing a call with the accumulator containing 3. The byte result is in the Y register. This entry call is applicable on the Electron only.
Accumulator=3
Request length of soft key expansion. The key number is held in the Y register and the length should be substituted for it. Again, an Electron-only call.

Language entry calls 2 and 3 are the Electron-specific ones and should not be trapped or tested for on a BBC-only item of firmware.

Languages and the Tube

Now that second processors are readily available it is essential that languages are written so that they will run across the Tube. This simply means that they are capable of relocating in the second processor and running correctly. If you write your languages correctly then this process will take place automatically. But what is correctly? Well, it simply means that all input/output processes should be performed using the operating system commands and memory should not be peeked and poked directly. Thus, the screen should be written to using OSWRCH and not by poking the ASCII character of a code there directly. For example, the letter A should be printed at the current cursor position, using

```
LDA #ASC("A")
JSR oswrch
```

and not by using poking such as

```
LDA #ASC("A")
STA screen+offset
```

To take advantage of the increased memory capacity offered by the second processor, a Hi version of the language you are writing may be required. This option is available simply by assembling your language coding so that it will run at a higher relocation address: &B800, for example, as with Hi-BASIC. The service entry point and its associated coding should remain assembled at the normal addresses as this is not copied across in the second processor by the Tube ROM and is required to function within the Beeb. Such a Hi version of your language would not run in the normal Beeb, however, due to the change in absolute addresses which would place it 'within' the MOS!

Chapter Five
The ROM Filing System

The ROM filing system is without doubt the least used of the three filing systems available on the BBC Micro. This is probably due to the lack of paged ROM software available in the ROM filing system format and the need for an EPROM programmer to allow the home user full access to it. However, the advent of the cheap, home-use EPROM programmer will make the ROM filing system a desirable feature for the serious user. Chapter 10 contains details on EPROM programmers and a suitable circuit and software if you wish to construct your own.

The ROM filing system, which is selected by typing in the operating system command

   *ROM <return>

may contain either BASIC or machine code programs that may be loaded, chained, or run as normal. Table 5.1 lists the commands and operating system calls available using the ROM filing system.

Table 5.1. ROM filing system commands and calls.

LOAD	
*CAT	
*EXEC	
*LOAD	
*RUN	
OSARGS	(filing system identification only)
OSBGET	
OSFILE	(save is not possible)
OSFIND	(output opening is not possible)

The number of files stored per ROM is limited only by the amount of space within the EPROM into which programs may be 'blown'. EPROMs may be 4K, 8K or 16K in length, and programs may run across the end and start of two EPROMs formatted correctly as long as the two EPROMs are placed sequentially within the Beeb, i.e. next to each other in order of priority.

The RFS ROM header

I have mentioned already that the files to be blown into an EPROM to use with the ROM filing system (RFS) file must be formatted in a special way. This is known as the ROM image. Before we examine this formatting we must provide a means for the ROM to be recognised and then to handle any RFS calls by the operating system. To allow this, the ROM image must be provided with a service entry and suitable code to handle the operating system's RFS call. Only two service entry calls are possible and these are service call 13 (&0D) and service call 14 (&0E).

Service call 13

This service call is the ROM filing system initialisation call. It is issued by the operating system when a filing system command is issued at the time when the RFS is the active filing system. The service call number is held in the accumulator on entry and the Y register contains a number which is 15 minus the number of the next ROM to be scanned. If this value is less than the number of the current ROM being investigated then the ROM should ignore the service call as the ROM has been investigated earlier. If it is not, the current ROM's number should be loaded into the accumulator. This is found at location &F4, which should then be placed in zero page location &F5. This action is an important step as it indicates to the MOS that RFS-formatted ROMs are present, otherwise future searches are liable to terminate if the MOS is led to believe that no such ROMs are present. The final act of the ROM header coding should be to place the start address of the ROM file data into the vector at &F6 and &F7. To complete the call and inform the MOS that the current ROM is now active, the call should return with the accumulator holding zero.

Service call 14

This call is a simple RFS get byte routine. To respond to this call, the current ROM must check location &F5. If this byte is equal to 15-?&F4, then the current ROM is indicated.

To extract the correct byte, the Y register must be cleared and used in post-indirect addressing to peek the byte held at the vectored address in &F6. The read byte should be returned in the Y register with the accumulator clear to indicate that the call has been serviced correctly.

The service call coding

Using the above information, writing the service call and header is quite straightforward. The first six bytes must contain the language and service entry jump addresses respectively. As there is no language entry, the first three bytes must be zero.

```
EQUB &00              \   No language entry so write
EQUW &0000            \   three zero bytes
JMP entry MOD 256+&8000   \   entry if file data start label
```

As we are forming the ROM image header in RAM rather than directly into the sideways ROM area, it is vitally important that the correct addresses, i.e. from &8000 onwards, are assembled. Thus, the JMP above is assembled correctly by adding &8000 to the low byte address of the file data start address. If your code header is extended by any considerable amount, it is important to check that the page boundary of &80 is not exceeded. If the file data 'entry' point moves to the next page, i.e. page &81, then the addition factor must be altered; thus the service jump address details would become

```
JMP entry MOD 256 + &8100
```

A suitable FN call could be included at this point to perform error checking if so desired.

The next byte should contain the ROM type byte. Referring to Chapter 2, we can see that bits 7 and 1 must be set to indicate that the ROM has a service entry point, though no language entry point. Thus the byte becomes 10000010 binary which is &82 hex. This is assembled in the header with

```
EQUB &82      \   type byte
```

Byte 7 must contain the copyright offset pointer. Assuming that the copyright message is labelled by 'offset', the mnemonic to assemble the correct byte is

```
EQUB   offset MOD 256      \   just need low byte of offset
```

The next byte is the version number which should be represented in hex. Unless this is an important feature for you to keep track of updated software, simply assemble &00 with

```
EQUB &00
```

The next sequence of bytes contain the ROM title string, i.e. the one that would be displayed if a *HELP was issued, presuming the RFS ROM can handle a *HELP. This is assembled with EQUS:

```
EQUS "RFS"      \   title string
```

This must be terminated with a zero byte:

```
EQUB &00      \   terminating byte
```

and followed by the copyright message, marked by the label 'offset':

```
.offset
EQUS "(C) Bruce Smith"        \   copyright string
```

and once again terminated by a zero byte:

```
EQUB &00      \   terminating byte
```

Having assembled the standard sideways ROM data as required by the MOS, the RFS service code can be dealt with, starting with the service call 13 code.

```
.entry
CMP #13                \   Acc holds service call. Is it 13?
BNE tryagain           \   if not branch over
PHA                    \   save accumulator service call code
TYA                    \   Y holds ROM number, move into acc
EOR #15                \   calculate 15-ROM number
CMP &F4                \   is it less than current ROM number?
BCC return             \   if C clear answer yes, ROM already
                       \   done so skip code
LDA #filename MOD 256  \   get low byte file start address
STA &F6                \   save in vector low byte
LDA # filename DIV 256 \   get high byte file start address
STA &F7                \   save in vector high byte
LDA &F4                \   get current ROM number
EOR #15                \   restore ROM number on entry
STA &F5                \   save and flag so can skip standard
                       \   paged ROMs
JMP restore+&5000      \   jump to restore (see next page)
                       \   &5000 added to get &8000+address
.return
PLA                    \   restore service type
.back
RTS                    \   and back to MOS
.tryagain              \   entry for next service type check
```

The above coding should not pose too many problems, though the +&5000 used as an argument in the calculation of the JMP address may be confusing. The &5000 must be added to the address of 'restore' to ensure that a correct address greater than &8000 is assembled. The above coding forms part of a much bigger ROM image formatting program presented towards the end of this chapter. The ROM image is created from &3000 by the program; adding &5000 to this provides the correct adjustment. The entry to 'restore' is provided in the coding below. The ROM byte request is handled as follows:

```
.tryagain            \  entry for next service test
CMP #&0E             \  is it ROM byte get?
BNE back             \  if not then branch to back
PHA                  \  save service call
LDA &F5              \  get 'current' ROM value
EOR #15              \  calculate 15-ROM number
CMP &F4              \  is it the same as this ROM number?
BNE return           \  no, it's another ROM so return
LDY #0               \  clear indexing register
LDA (&F6),Y          \  read byte into accumulator
TAY                  \  move into Y register
INC &F6              \  increment low byte vector
BNE restore          \  branch if not zero
INC &F7              \  else increment high byte of vector
.restore
PLA                  \  pull service type off stack
LDA #0               \  clear accumulator to indicate
                     \  that service has been performed
RTS                  \  and back to MOS
.filename            \  start of file data
```

Again, there is nothing too difficult in the coding. The label 'filename' is used to mark the start of the first program file within the ROM.

The above service call handling routine is in its basic form, and is the minimum required. It can, of course, be expanded to include a *HELP service call, details of which are provided at the end of the chapter. Expanding the service call polling does eat up space, thereby reducing the amount available to the memory-gobbling ROM image. Details of files stored within ROMs can always be ascertained with the *CAT command.

The ROM image

The ROM image starts directly after the service call header. It is constructed in a manner similar to that used by the cassette filing system, using a block structure. Each block consists of a header followed by the file data. The header construction is important and is laid out as follows:

(a) A synchronisation byte, &2A (ASCII"*").
(b) Filename, up to ten characters long.
(c) A filename terminating zero byte, &00.
(d) File load address.
(e) File execution address.
(f) Two-byte block number.
(g) Two-byte block length.
(h) File flag.

(i) Address of first byte after end of file.

(h) Two-byte header Cyclic Redundancy Check.

The synchronisation byte must always be &2A. This is ASCII "*" so that the filename always looks as though it was in *RUN format, i.e. *FILENAME. A filename cannot be a null string so must contain a minimum of just one character though it must not exceed ten characters in length. The filename is terminated with a zero byte.

The load and execution addresses occupy four bytes, the low byte being stored first. The high two bytes provide space for a second processor relocation address. The block number and length details consist of two bytes stored low byte first.

The file flag provides details about the file stored at bit level. Three bits are used thus:

B7: If this bit is set, it indicates that this is the last block of the current file.

B6: If this bit is set, it indicates that this block contains no data.

B0: This is the protection bit. If this bit is set the file can only be *RUN.

The function of bit 6 (B6) may seem odd at first sight. An empty block can be created at ROM image formation time if the file is opened for output and then closed before any data can be written to it using BPUT.

The header Cyclic Redundancy Check (CRC) is contained in two bytes, stored high byte first. The CRC is an error check against data corruption. Each CRC is unique to the item it refers to as it is calculated from all the data that it relates to! A suitable algorithm for calculating the CRC of a piece of data would be

High Byte = Data EOR High Byte
FOR Loop=1 TO 8
Carry=0
IF (msb of High Byte=1) THEN High AND Low Bytes EOR &810:
    Carry=1
High AND Low Bytes=(High AND Low Bytes*2 + Carry) AND
    &FFFF
NEXT Loop

After the header comes the file block which is, for a full block, 256 bytes in length. The last block of a file may be shorter if the length of the file is not exactly divisible by 256. The length of the block is specified in the two header bytes, block length. The file data is terminated by two CRC bytes which are the data CRC, calculated as for the header CRC.

To save ROM space, the header of file blocks, other than the first and last file blocks, may be abbreviated by a single character, the hash, '#' which is ASCII &43. If a hash header is used, the MOS assumes that the header details are the same as specified in the first file header block.

Finally, the end of the ROM image – that is, the byte after the last file of the last program – is marked by an end-of-ROM marker, typically a '+', ASCII code &2B. This marker may only be omitted if the ROM image spans over to another ROM which must be positioned as the next ROM number in order of priority.

ROM filing system vectors

As is usual on the BBC Micro, indirect entry to the RFS processing is performed via the standard page two vectors. Table 5.2 lists the vectors changed by initialisation of the ROM filing system and the address contained within them for the 1.2 OS.

Table 5.2. The *ROM vectors.

Vector	Address	Indirection address
FILEV	&212	&F27D
ARGSV	&214	&F18E
BGETV	&216	&F4C9
BPUTV	&218	&F529
GPPBV	&21A	&FFA6
FINDV	&21C	&F3CA
FSCV	&21E	&F1B1

This table indicates that provision for a OSBPUT has been included in the RFS vectored entry but this is rather meaningless as a ROM may only be read and not written to, unlike RAM.

The ROM image formatter

Program 5.1 is a tried and tested ROM image formatting program. As it stands it will work with either a disc- or cassette-based system, though the former is preferable from the operator's point of view. The program will read in specified files from the storage medium in use and format them into a ROM image. As written, the program assumes that an 8K image is required though it may be any length up to this value. The image may be converted to encompass 16K chips, and details on doing this are provided in the program description. If the total file image length exceeds the EPROM storage capacity, the user is informed and the last file entered is not accepted. On completion, the ROM image may be saved if so desired, to facilitate blowing into EPROM. Before running the program, read the RFS running notes later in this chapter.

```
   10 REM ROM Filing System Formatter
   20 REM (c) Bruce Smith
   30 REM September 1984
   40 REM The BBC Micro ROM Book
   50 :
   60 ON ERROR GOTO 2240
   70 MODE7
   80 DIM block% 20,name% 20,mcode% 250
   90 size=&2000
  100 buffer%=&3000
  110 PROCassemble
  120 PRINT CHR$(130);CHR$(141);SPC(9);
  130 PRINT "RFS FORMATTER"
  140 PRINT CHR$(130);CHR$(141);SPC(9);
  150 PRINT "RFS FORMATTER"
  160 PRINT'CHR$(129);SPC(6);
  170 PRINT "(c) Bruce Smith 1984"'
  180 PRINTTAB(0,24);CHR$(131);SPC(7);
  190 PRINT "Press RETURN to end";TAB(5,
5)
  200 VDU 28,0,23,39,5
  210 PROCromhead(buffer%)
  220 REPEAT
  230 INPUT"Enter file name : " $name%
  240  IF $name%<>"" THEN IF FNinfo THEN
 PROCformat
  250 UNTIL $name%=""
  260 ?marker%=ASC("+")
  270 finish%=marker%+1
  280 PROCsave
  290 VDU 26
  300 CLS
  310 END
  320 :
  330 DEF PROCformat
  340 LOCAL block%
  350 block%=0
  360 IF extent%>256 THEN PROChandle
  370 PROCfilehead(marker%,name%,load%,e
xecution%,block%,&80,extent%)
  380 CLOSE#channel%
  390 ENDPROC
  400 :
  410 DEF FNinfo
  420 LOCAL L$,tape%
  430 A%=0:Y%=0
  440 tape%=(USR &FFDA AND &FF)<4
  450 channel%=OPENUP($name%)
  460 IF tape% THEN PROCtapedetails
  470 IF NOT tape% THEN PROCnottape
```

```
  480 nextfile%=&8000+marker%-buffer%+(L
EN($name%)+23)-(LEN($name%)+23)*(extent%
>256)-3*(extent%>512)*(((extent%-1) DIV
256)-1)+extent%
  490 space%=(nextfile%<&8000+size-1)AND
(channel%<>0)
  500 IF NOT space% THEN PRINT CHR$(7);"
ERROR"'"File not found / File to big":CL
OSE#channel%
  510 =space%
  520 :
  530 DEF PROCfilehead(position%.file%.l
address%,execaddr%,bcount%,flag%,length%
)
  540 LOCAL pos%
  550 ?position%=ASC("*")
  560 position%=position%+1
  570 $position%=$file%
  580 pos%=LEN($file%)+position%
  590 ?pos%=0
  600 pos%!1=laddress%
  610 pos%!5=execaddr%
  620 pos%!9=bcount%
  630 pos%!11=length%
  640 pos%?13=flag%
  650 pos%!14=nextfile%
  660 ?&84=pos%-position%+18
  665 !&80=position%
  670 CALL  docrc
  680 pos%!18=!&82
  690 marker%=pos%+20
  700 PROCgetdata(length%)
  710 block%=block%+1
  720 ENDPROC
  730 :
  740 DEF PROCgetdata(length%)
  750 LOCAL pos%
  760 FOR pos%=0 TO length%-1
  770 marker%?pos%=BGET#channel%
  780 NEXTpos%
  790 !&80=marker%
  800 ?&84=length%
  810 CALL docrc
  820 marker%!length%=!&82
  830 extent%=extent%-length%
  840 marker%=marker%+length%+2
  850 ENDPROC
  860 :
  870 DEF PROChash
  880 ?marker%=ASC("#")
```

```
 890 marker%=marker%+1
 900 PROCgetdata(&100)
 910 block%=block%+1
 920 ENDPROC
 930 :
 940 DEF PROCassemble
 950 address=&80
 960 crc1=&82
 970 crc2=&83
 980 FOR pass=0 TO 2 STEP 2
 990 P%=mcode%
1000 [OPT pass
1010 .docrc
1020         LDA #0
1030         STA crc1
1040         STA crc2
1050         TAY
1060 .next
1070         LDA crc1
1080         EOR (address).Y
1090         STA crc1
1100         LDX #8
1110 .again
1120         LDA crc1
1130         ROL A
1140         BCC over
1150         LDA crc1
1160         EOR #8
1170         STA crc1
1180         LDA crc2
1190         EOR #&10
1200         STA crc2
1210 .over
1220         ROL crc2
1230         ROL crc1
1240         DEX
1250         BNE again
1260         INY
1270         CPY crc2+1
1280         BNE next
1290         RTS
1300 ]
1310 NEXT pass
1320 ENDPROC
1330 :
1340 DEF PROCromhead (header%)
1350 FOR pass=0 TO 3 STEP 2
1360 P%=header%
1370 [OPT pass
1380         EQUW 0
1390         EQUB 0
```

```
1400          JMP entry MOD 256+&8000
1410          EQUB &82
1420          EQUB offset   MOD 256
1430          EQUB 0
1440          EQUS "RFS"
1450 .offset
1460          EQUB 0
1470          EQUS "(C) Bruce Smith"
1480          EQUB 0
1490 .entry
1500          CMP #13
1510          BNE tryagain
1520          PHA
1530          TYA
1540          EOR #15
1550          CMP &F4
1560          BCC return
1570          LDA #filename MOD 256
1580          STA &F6
1590          LDA #&80
1600          STA &F7
1610          LDA &F4
1620          EOR #15
1630          STA &F5
1640          JMP restore+&5000
1650 .return
1660          PLA
1670 .back
1680          RTS
1690 .tryagain
1700          CMP #&0E
1710          BNE back
1720          PHA
1730          LDA &F5
1740          EOR #15
1750          CMP &F4
1760          BNE return
1770          LDY #0
1780          LDA (&F6).Y
1790          TAY
1800          INC &F6
1810          BNE restore
1820          INC &F7
1830 .restore
1840          PLA
1850          LDA #0
1860          RTS
1870 .filename
1880 ]
1890 NEXT
1900 marker%=header%+&58
```

```
1910 ENDPROC
1920 :
1930 DEF PROChandle
1940 PROCfilehead(marker%,name%,load%,e
xecution%,block%,0,&100)
1950 IF extent%>256 THEN REPEAT:PROChas
h:UNTIL extent%<=256
1960 ENDPROC
1970 :
1980 DEF PROCtapedetails
1990 load%=!&3BE
2000 execution%=!&3C2
2010 INPUT'"      Type file length - &" L
$
2020 extent%=EVAL("&"+L$)
2030 ENDPROC
2040 :
2050 DEF PROCnottape
2060 !block%=name%
2070 A%=5:X%=block% MOD 256
2080 Y%=block% DIV 256
2090 CALL &FFDD
2100 load%=block%!2
2110 execution%=block%!6
2120 extent%=block%!10
2130 ENDPROC
2140 :
2150 DEF PROCsave
2160 PRINT"Do you wish to save formatte
d file(s)?"
2170 key%=GET
2180 IF key%<>ASC("Y") THEN ENDPROC
2190 PRINT"Saving current ROM files"
2200 *SAVE ROMFILE 3000 5000
2210 ENDPROC
2220 :
2230 ***** ERROR HANDLER *******
2240 CLOSE #0
2250 VDU 26,7
2260 CLS
2270 REPORT
2280 PRINT" ERROR at line ";ERL
2290 END
```

Program 5.1. The ROM Image Formatter.

Program description

A line-by-line description of the formatter program now follows. This should enable you to make any modifications you require with the minimum of fuss.

Line 60: Set up error handler.

Line 70: Use Teletext mode.

Line 80: Dimension space for parameter block, filename string and machine code storage.

Line 90: Set size of EPROM to 8K. To form 16K image, alter this value to &4000 or &1000 for a 4K device.

Line 100: ROM image is stored from &3000.

Lines 110 to 200: Set up screen headings and text window.

Line 210: Form the ROM service header.

Line 220: Set up main program loop.

Line 230: Get name of file to be formatted.

Line 240: Get catalogue details and format file if present.

Line 250: Repeat loop until terminated by entry of null string filename.

Line 260: Poke end of ROM marker at end of file image.

Line 270: calculate its address in image, for reference.

Line 280: Save ROM image.

Line 290: Restore all default windows.

Line 300: Clear screen.

Line 310: End of program.

Line 330: Entry for PROCformat.

Line 340: Set up local variable, block%.

Line 350: Set to zero.

Line 360: if the file's length exceeds 256 bytes then call hash heading entry.

Line 370: Format last block of file.

Line 380: Close file reading channel.

Line 390: End of procedure.

Line 410: Entry for FNinfo.

Line 420: Set up local variables.

Line 430: Clear Accumulator and X Register via A% and X%.

Line 440: Read current filing system via OSARGS. If less than 4 must be *TAPE.

Line 450: Open up channel for reading.

Line 460: If tape filing system then read file details.

Line 470: If disc filing system read file details.

Line 480: Calculate address of last byte plus one of file.

Line 490: Calculate space remaining in ROM image.

Line 500: If negative value then there's not enough space for current file so issue a warning and refuse file!

Line 510: End of function.

Line 530: Entry to PROCfilehead.

Line 540: Initialise local variable.

Line 550: Poke synchronisation byte at start of header.

Line 560: Update position in header.

Line 570: Write filename to header.

Line 580: Update position in header.

Line 590: Poke filename terminator byte.

Line 600: Pling file load address in header.

Line 610: Pling file's execution address in header.

Line 620: Pling block number in header.

Line 630: Pling block length in header.

Line 640: Poke header flag byte in header.

Line 650: Pling address of end of file plus one in header.

Line 660: Poke low byte of header's start address for use by CRC calculation routine.

Line 670: Calculate header CRC.

Line 680: Pling header CRC in header.

Line 690: Calculate start of current file to be placed after header in image.

Line 700: Read file data from medium and poke into image.

Line 710: Increment block number.

Line 720: End of procedure.

Line 740: Entry to PROCgetdata

Line 750: Initialise local variable.

Line 760: Set up byte reading loop.

Line 770: Read byte from file and poke into position in ROM image.

Line 780: Repeat loop until all bytes in block read.

Line 790: Place start address of block of data just read in zero page for use in calculation of data CRC.

Line 800: Poke total number of bytes in current block into zero page.

Line 810: Calculate data CRC.

Line 820: Pling data CRC onto end of current block data in ROM image.

Line 830: Calculate number of bytes remaining in current file.

Line 840: Update position in ROM image to point to byte after CRC.

Line 850: End of procedure.

Line 870: Entry to PROChash.

Line 880: Poke hash into position in ROM image.

Line 890: Update position in image.

Line 900: Get and store 256 bytes of file data.

Line 910: Increment block count.

Line 920: End of procedure.

Line 940: Entry to PROCassemble to set up CRC calculation code.

Lines 950 to 970: Initialise assembler variables.

Line 980: Two-pass assembly – no listing.

Line 990: Assemble code in predimensioned area.

Line 1000: Entry point to CRC calculation.

Line 1020: Load zero into accumulator.

Lines 1030 to 1040: Clear CRC high and low bytes.

Line 1050: Clear indexing register.

Line 1060: Main code loop entry point.

Line 1070: Get CRC high byte.

Line 1080: Exclusive OR with byte in block.

Line 1090: Save result in CRC high byte.
Line 1100: Set bit count to 8.
Line 1110: Inner bit count loop entry point.
Line 1120: Get high byte CRC.
Line 1130: Rotate one bit to the left and into carry flag.
Line 1140: Branch over if no carry.
Line 1150: If bit moving out get high byte again.
Line 1160: Subtract accumulator from 8.
Line 1170: Save in high byte position.
Line 1180: Get low byte.
Line 1190: Move carry bit into low byte CRC.
Line 1200: Save result.
Line 1210: Entry to over if no carry.
Lines 1220 to 1230: Perform single byte rotation on 16-bit shift register.
Line 1240: Decrement bit count.
Line 1250: Do until all bits done.
Line 1260: Increment index to point to next byte.
Line 1270: Have all bytes been evaluated?
Line 1280: Branch if answer is no.
Line 1290: Else return back to BASIC.
Line 1320: End of procedure.
Line 1340: Entry to PROCromhead.
Line 1350: Two-pass assembly loop initialisation.
Line 1360: Assemble code at start of ROM image.
Lines 1380 and 1390: Assemble three zeros as there is no language entry
      point.
Line 1400: Assemble service entry point jump address.
Line 1410: Assemble &82 as ROM type.
Line 1420: Assemble copyright offset pointer.
Line 1430: Assemble binary version number.
Line 1440: Assemble ROM title string.
Line 1450: Label marking offset.
Line 1460: Title string terminating byte.
Line 1470: Assemble copyright string.
Line 1480: Assemble terminating byte.
Line 1490: Label marking service call entry point.
Line 1500: Was it ROM initialisation service call?
Line 1510: Branch to try again if not.
Line 1520: Save service call type on the hardware stack.
Line 1530: Transfer logical ROM number into the accumulator.
Line 1540: Subtract it from 15.
Line 1550: Is it less than current ROM number?
Line 1560: Yes, therefore ROM already done so pass over.
Line 1570: Get low byte address of start of ROM image program(s).
Line 1580: Store in &F6.

Line 1590: Get high byte address of start of the ROM image program(s).

Line 1600: Save in &F7.

Line 1610: Get current ROM number.

Line 1620: Subtract it from 15.

Line 1630: Save in &F5 to indicate that this ROM has been initialised.

Line 1640: Jump to return coding.

Line 1650: Entry point to return back to BASIC.

Line 1660: Restore service call code.

Line 1670: Entry for branches to back.

Line 1680: Return to BASIC.

Line 1690: Entry to test for service call 14.

Line 1700: Was it get byte from ROM call?

Line 1710: If not then branch to back.

Line 1720: Push call number onto hardware stack.

Line 1730: Get logical ROM number.

Line 1740: Subtract it from 15.

Line 1750: Is it the same as the current ROM's number?

Line 1760: If not then branch to return.

Line 1770: Initialise post-indexing register to zero.

Line 1780: Get byte from within current ROM.

Line 1790: Transfer it into the Y register.

Line 1800: Increment low byte value of vectored address.

Line 1810: If not zero, branch two bytes forward to restore.

Line 1820: Else increment page of vectored address.

Line 1830: Entry to restore branches.

Line 1840: Pull stack to balance previous push.

Line 1850: Clear accumulator to indicate that service has been provided.

Line 1860: Return back to BASIC.

Line 1870: Start address of ROM image file data, i.e. program(s).

Line 1900: Update marker to point to first 'free' byte in ROM image. If extra coding is placed in the service call processing header then this value will change!

Line 1910: End of procedure.

Line 1930: Entry to PROChandle.

Line 1940: Do first block of file.

Line 1950: Do rest of file blocks except the very last one which is indicated when the value of extent% drops below 256.

Line 1960: End of procedure.

Line 1980: Entry to PROCtape details.

Line 1990: Get load address of file from block zero RAM.

Line 2000: Get execution address as well.

Line 2010: Get total length of file from user.

Line 2020: Convert ASCII string into a hexadecimal value.

Line 2030: End of procedure.

Line 2050: Entry to PROCnottape.

Line 2060: Place address of filename into first two bytes of parameter block.

Lines 2070 to 2080: Place address of parameter block into index registers and call code into accumulator.

Line 2090: Call OSFILE to read catalogue information of specified file.

Line 2100: Get load address of file.

Line 2110: Get execution address of file.

Line 2120: Get total length of file.

Line 2130: End of procedure.

Line 2150: Entry to PROCsave.

Lines 2160–2180: Find if ROM image is to be saved.

Line 2190: Print saving message.

Line 2200: Save ROM image.

Line 2210: End of procedure.

Line 2230: Error-handling routine.

Line 2240: Close all open channels.

Line 2250: Restore text window and issue bleep.

Line 2260: Clear screen.

Line 2270: Report error message.

Line 2280: Print error number and line.

Line 2290: End of program.

The procedures

The formatter includes eleven procedures which form the basis of the program. The function of each is as follows:

PROCformat: This procedure first tests to see if there is more than one block in a file. If this is the case then PROChandle is called. On return from PROChandle only the last block remains to be formatted so this is undertaken by the call to PROCfilehead. The last action of this procedure is to close the open reading channel.

PROCfilehead: This procedure constructs a detailed block header for the first and last blocks of a file, including the calculation of the header CRCs.

PROCgetdata: As its name implies, this procedure reads each byte of data from a file and pokes it into the correct position in the ROM image. It also provides the data CRC value.

PROChash: This procedure is called for all file blocks except the first and last. It creates the abbreviated hash header for the intermediate files and also initialises each PROCgetdata call to fetch 256 bytes, in addition to keeping track of the block count.

PROCassemble: This simply assembles the machine code that calculates the CRC for both headers and data bytes.

PROCromhead: Assembles the ROM head details required by the MOS and also the service call polling as required. These are assembled directly in the front of the ROM image.

PROChandle: This creates the first block image of a file and then controls the formatting of the intermediate blocks but not the very last block of a file.
PROCtapedetails: This reads the load and execution addresses of a tape-based file from block zero RAM. It accepts input for the file length and converts it into a hexadecimal value.
PROCnottape: Reads the catalogue information of the specified file from a disc using OSFILE.
PROCsave: Saves the ROM image to the current filing medium.
FNinfo: This is the only function in the program and it ascertains which filing system is in use and calls the relative procedure to read the file's catalogue details. In addition, it calculates whether the current file will fit into the remaining ROM image space.

Using the formatter

The RFS formatter is simple to use, though a certain amount of preparation is required by tape users. If you are using tape before you run the program it is necessary to ascertain the length of each program file as this value cannot be read from within block zero RAM as with the load and execution addresses. To do this, first ensure that the programs you wish to format are together on the same tape. Now enable detailed catalogue messages by entering.

   *OPT 1,2

The next step is to catalogue the tape. On completion of each file a long catalogue message will be issued. This takes the form:

   Filename 0C 0CF6 FFFF0E00 FFFF8023

Reading from left to right, we have the program filename, the block number, the file length, the file load address and the file's execution address. In the above example, we would need to note the value &CF6 (all above values are in hex) as the file length. This process should be repeated for each program file and the tape rewound to the start of the very first file. With these values at hand the main formatter can be run.

   On running, the screen will clear and you will be asked for the name of the first file. This should be entered and the return key pressed. If a disc filing system is in use, the appropriate file will be accessed and formatted into the ROM image. If a tape system is being used, the first block will be loaded and then you will be prompted to enter the file length previously noted as already described. This value should be entered in hex though it is not necessary to include the '&' as this will be prompted with the input request. After entering this and pressing the return key the rest of the file will be loaded.

   After the file has been read in and formatted you will be prompted for another file name. The above process should be repeated as required. If at any time the file length exceeds the amount of space remaining in the ROM image, an error message will be issued and the program will prompt for a new filename. Once all the files you want formatted have been completed, simply press the return key. The next filename prompt is then issued to complete the construction of the ROM image. You will then be asked if you wish to save the ROM image; pressing the Y key will perform this task, otherwise the program will end.

Checking the image

As the saying goes, the proof of the pudding is in the eating. There is no eating involved here but you could feel a bit of a pudding if you waste several EPROMs trying to implement the ROM filing system when the formatter is not functioning correctly. So before trying to blow a ROM image into a EPROM it is well worth going through a dummy run and examining carefully a hex dump of the ROM image. To help the process, the following pages are devoted to forming and checking a standard ROM image.

The first step is to enter and save the following short test program:

```
10 REM AAAAAA
20 REM BBBBBB
30 REM CCCCCC
40 REM DDDDDD
```

The program should be entered exactly as shown, with single spaces between each line number and REM and immediately after each REM. The program occupies &36 bytes so, to ensure that it is entered correctly, enter:

PRINT ~(TOP–PAGE)

The value printed out should be 36 (this value is in hex). If this is not the case, ensure that you have not entered any extra spaces at the end of a line. Once you are satisfied that all is well, save the program using the filename "TEST", thus:

SAVE "TEST"

Access to a hexadecimal and ASCII dump routine is vital. If you have a suitable utility available in a sideways ROM then all is well. Just in case you don't then Program 5.2 will provide you with such a routine. Enter and test this then save it to disc or tape.

```
10 REM Hex and ASCII Dumper
20 REM (C) Bruce Smith
30 REM September 1984
40 REM The BBC Micro ROM Book
50 :
60 @%=0
```

```
 70 FOR P%=&3000 TO &30FF STEP 8
 80 PRINT~P%;"   ";
 90 FOR N%=0 TO 7
100 IF P%?N%<16 PRINT"0";
110 PRINT~P%?N%;" ";
120 NEXT
130 PRINT"   ";
140 FOR N%=0 TO 7
150 A%=P%?N%
160 IF A%<32 OR A%>127 PRINT".";  ELSE
PRINT CHR$(A%);
170 NEXT
180 NEXT
```

Program 5.2. Hex and ASCII Dump Program.

The next stage is to enter the formatter, and then ensure that the buffer area is clear by entering the following one-liner in immediate mode:

FOR N%=&3000 TO &4000 STEP 4:!N%=0:NEXT

This process is not normally required but it will enable us to see where the ROM image ends clearly. The next step is to run the formatter and format the TEST program *twice*. In other words, you need to type in the filename twice in response to the prompt for it. If you are using tape this will mean rewinding the tape slightly before starting it going again. Tape users will also need to enter the file length when requested. On being prompted for a filename for the third time, press the return key, and end the program by pressing the N key when asked if you wish to save the image.

The next stage in the process is to load the memory dump program. Running this will produce a dump of the ROM image as shown in Fig. 5.1. This should be examined closely byte by byte and the following description should help.

The bytes from &3000 to &3057 contain the ROM service call header as described earlier. The title and copyright strings can clearly be seen in the ASCII dump section on the right-hand side of the listing. The opcode for RTS, &60, to terminate the polling is located at the last byte in this section. If this is not the case check your assembly listing in PROCromhead.

The line starting 3058 contains the synchronisation byte, &2A, followed by the ASCII filename and then the terminator byte, &00.

The next four bytes, the last two in the above line and the first two in the line beginning 3060 hold the program load address. This is stored low byte first. The actual value here will depend on the setting of PAGE on your Beeb. On mine it is &1A00; normally on micros fitted with a DFS it will be &1900 and &0E00 on a tape system. The next four bytes hold the execution address, again low byte first. As my Beeb uses BASIC II the value is 23 80 FF FF; if you have BASIC I then the first number will be &19. The last two bytes in the line are the block number; both are zero, indicating that this is block zero.

```
3000 : 00 00 00 4C 1D 80 82 0C   ...L....
3008 : 00 52 46 53 00 28 43 29   .RFS.(C)
3010 : 20 42 72 75 63 65 20 53   Bruce S
3018 : 6D 69 74 68 00 C9 0D D0   mith....
3020 : 1B 48 98 49 0F C5 F4 90   .H.I....
3028 : 11 A9 58 85 F6 A9 80 85   ..X.....
3030 : F7 A5 F4 49 0F 85 F5 4C   ...I...L
3038 : 54 80 68 60 C9 0E D0 FB   T.h`....
3040 : 48 A5 F5 49 0F C5 F4 D0   H..I....
3048 : F1 A0 00 B1 F6 A8 E6 F6   ........
3050 : D0 02 E6 F7 68 A9 00 60   ....h..`
3058 : 2A 54 45 53 54 00 00 1A   *TEST...
3060 : FF FF 23 80 FF FF 00 00   ..#.....
3068 : 36 00 80 A9 80 00 00 7A   6......z
3070 : AE 0D 00 0A 0D 20 F4 20   ..... .
3078 : 41 41 41 41 41 41 0D 00   AAAAAA..
3080 : 14 0D 20 F4 20 42 42 42   .. . BBB
3088 : 42 42 42 0D 00 1E 0D 20   BBB....
3090 : F4 20 43 43 43 43 43 43   . CCCCCC
3098 : 0D 00 28 0D 20 F4 20 44   ..(. . D
30A0 : 44 44 44 44 44 0D FF 82   DDDDD...
30A8 : 6B 2A 54 45 53 54 00 00   k*TEST..
30B0 : 1A FF FF 23 80 FF FF 00   ...#....
30B8 : 00 36 00 80 FA 80 00 00   .6......
30C0 : B4 D2 0D 00 0A 0D 20 F4   ...... .
30C8 : 20 41 41 41 41 41 41 0D   AAAAAA.
30D0 : 00 14 0D 20 F4 20 42 42   ... . BB
30D8 : 42 42 42 42 0D 00 1E 0D   BBBB....
30E0 : 20 F4 20 43 43 43 43 43   . CCCCC
30E8 : 43 0D 00 28 0D 20 F4 20   C..(. .
30F0 : 44 44 44 44 44 44 0D FF   DDDDDD..
30F8 : 82 6B 2B 00 00 00 00 00   .k+.....
```

Fig. 5.1. Hex and ASCII dump of ROM image.

The line beginning 3068 contains the file length in the first two bytes, 36 00 in this instance – low byte first, obviously! The next byte, 80, is the block byte, followed by four bytes which contain the address of the byte after the end of the current file, and this should be as shown. The final byte in the line plus the first byte in the line beginning 3070 is the header CRC.

The test program is then stored in file form from 3071 to 30A6, with the last byte &FF being the program TOP. The next two bytes at 30A7 and 30A8 contain the file data CRC.

The header for the second file then follows and not surprisingly assumes the same format as just described!

The final byte in the ROM image is the end of ROM marker, &2B, located at &30FA.

Hash headers

Files that consist of several blocks may have their intermediate block headers replaced by a hash header which, in fact, just consists of a hash, ASCII code &23. In the dump below from a ROM image of the formatter itself, the hash header occupies the byte at 3174.

```
3158 : 29 3B 89 2B 39 29 3B 0D  );.(9);.
3160 : 00 82 17 F1 20 22 52 46  .... "RF
3168 : 53 20 46 4F 52 4D 41 54  S FORMAT
3170 : 54 45 A9 F8 23 52 22 20  TE..#R"
3178 : 20 0D 00 8C 1A F1 20 BD  ..... .
3180 : 28 31 33 30 29 3B BD 28  (130):.(
```

Chapter Six
ROM Vectors

When designing ROM firmware, you may wish to add facilities that are automatically accessed by the MOS as and when required. When, for example, an error occurs during program operation, the Beeb prints out the relevant error message. It would be nice, however, to add a patch that would call the routine in your sideways ROM to print out the erroneous line and perhaps even high-light the error itself. Similarly, filing system ROMs, such as disc filing systems, must be accessible from the calling program or command. However, calls cannot be made directly by a simple JSR command as the particular address is within a different ROM. A mechanism exists in the MOS whereby vectors may be altered to point into the MOS which will handle transfer of control from the current ROM to the routine in the relevant ROM and then switch back to the original ROM. This facility is called 'extended vector' entry.

Each of the twenty-seven vectors implemented on the Beeb is allocated a number such that the physical address of the vector is located at

&200+(2*vector number)

To point a vector into the operating system's extended vector processing routine, the vector itself must be made to point to

&FF00+(3*vector number)

Table 6.1 lists the actual entry points to which each vector must be made to point to be processed correctly.

Table 6.1. Extended vectors.

Vector	Location	Entended vector entry point
USERV	&200	&FF00
BRKV	&202	&FF03
IRQ1V	&204	&FF06
IRQ2V	&206	&FF09
CLIV	&208	&FF0C

BYTEV	&20A	&FF0F
WORDV	&20C	&FF12
WRCHV	&20E	&FF15
RDCHV	&210	&FF18
FILEV	&212	&FF1B
ARGSV	&214	&FF1E
BGETV	&216	&FF21
BPUTV	&218	&FF24
GBPBV	&21A	&FF27
FINDV	&21C	&FF2A
FSCV	&21E	&FF2D
EVENTV	&220	&FF30
UPTV	&222	&FF33
NETV	&224	&FF36
VDUV	&226	&FF39
KEYV	&228	&FF3C
INSV	&22A	&FF3F
REMV	&22C	&FF42
CNPV	&22E	&FF45
IND1V	&230	&FF48
IND2V	&232	&FF4B
IND3V	&234	&FF4E

To point the BRKV into the correct extended vector processing entry point, the address &FF03 must be placed in the vector at &202. In assembler terms this is simply

```
LDA #&03      \   get low byte address
STA &202      \   place in low byte of vector
LDA #&FF      \   get high byte address
STA &203      \   place in high byte of vector
```

As the table above shows, each extended vector entry point is offset by three bytes from the next. This is to allow the instruction JSR &FF51 to be assembled (N.B. for 1.2OS only, it may vary on other operating systems). This address marks the start of the processing coding.

The MOS needs to know which ROM to page in and just which address to call in it. Space is provided in RAM for this information in an area called the 'extended vector space', the start address of which is ascertained by issuing an OSBYTE call as follows:

```
LDA #&A8
LDX #&00
LDY #&FF
JSR osbyte
```

The call will return with the start address of the extended vector space in the index registers. In OS1.2 this address is &D9F.

Each vector is allocated three bytes in the extended vector space. The byte corresponding to each is found by calculating

Vector space + 3*vector number

These bytes must have the following information poked into them:

(a) Low byte of address in ROM
(b) High byte of address in ROM
(c) ROM number – copied from &F4

To place the address &CAFE into the BRKV for the current ROM so that it will trap BRKs, the following code would suffice:

```
STX address        \  save low byte space address
STY address+1      \  save high byte space address
LDY #3             \  start of BRKV extended vector space
LDA #&FE           \  low byte
STA (address),Y    \  place in space
INY
LDA #&CA           \  get high byte
STA (address),Y    \  place in space
INY
LDA &F4            \  get ROM identity
STA (address),Y    \  place in space
```

To allow this ROM to catch all BRKs this coding must be executed each time the system is reset. Trapping service call 1 would be an appropriate manner in which to do this.

Chapter Seven
The TOOLKIT Interpreter

One of the best ways of learning and improving your machine code programming techniques is to disassemble and study machine code written by professional programmers. This concept can readily be applied to learning how to write sideways ROM software, so this chapter is devoted entirely to a case study, a byte by byte examination of the Beebug TOOLKIT ROM. Figure 7.1 provides a straight disassembly listing. The listing has been produced using EXMON and can be broken down into four separate columns giving the following information:

(a) Hexadecimal address.
(b) Opcode and relevant operand(s) in hexadecimal.
(c) Equivalent ASCII characters. (A full-stop is printed if the character is not convertible into ASCII.)
(d) The mnemonics.

The line of code at &8042 would be presented as:

8042   B5   4E   .N   LDA &4E,X

Thus the columns are as follows:

8042	The hexadecimal address.
B5 4E	The opcode and operand in hex.
.N	Their ASCII equivalents. B5 is not convertible and is represented by the full-stop.
LDA &4E,X	The mnemonics.

```
8000  00           .      BRK
8001  00           .      BRK
8002  00           .      BRK
8003  4C 25 80  L%.       JMP &8025
8006  82           .      ???
8007  15 00        ..     ORA &00,X
8009  54           T      ???
800A  4F           O      ???
800B  4F           O      ???
800C  4C 4B 49  LKI       JMP &494B
```

```
800F 54          T      ???
8010 00          .      BRK
8011 31 2E       1.     AND (&2E),Y
8013 32          2      ???
8014 32          2      ???
8015 00          .      BRK
8016 28          (      PLP
8017 43          C      ???
8018 29 31       )1     AND #&31
801A 39 38 33    983    AND &3338,Y
801D 20 42 65    Be     JSR &6542
8020 65 62       eb     ADC &62
8022 75 67       ug     ADC &67,X
8024 00          .      BRK
8025 48          H      PHA
8026 8A          .      TXA
8027 48          H      PHA
8028 98          .      TYA
8029 48          H      PHA
802A AD 03 02    ...    LDA &0203
802D 48          H      PHA
802E AD 02 02    ...    LDA &0202
8031 48          H      PHA
8032 A5 19       ..     LDA &19
8034 48          H      PHA
8035 A5 1A       ..     LDA &1A
8037 48          H      PHA
8038 A5 F2       ..     LDA &F2
803A 85 19       ..     STA &19
803C A5 F3       ..     LDA &F3
803E 85 1A       ..     STA &1A
8040 A2 09       ..     LDX #&09
8042 B5 4E       .N     LDA &4E,X
8044 48          H      PHA
8045 CA          .      DEX
8046 10 FA       ..     BPL &8042
8048 BA          .      TSX
8049 BD 11 01    ...    LDA &0111,X
804C CA          .      DEX
804D CA          .      DEX
804E B8          .      CLV
804F C9 09       ..     CMP #&09
8051 F0 6A       .j     BEQ &80BD
8053 C9 01       ..     CMP #&01
8055 D0 1B       ..     BNE &8072
8057 A2 00       ..     LDX #&00
8059 86 08       ..     STX &08
805B 86 09       ..     STX &09
805D 8E F5 0A    ...    STX &0AF5
8060 8E F6 0A    ...    STX &0AF6
```

```
8063 8E FF 0A  ...      STX &0AFF
8066 CA        .        DEX
8067 8E F4 0A  ...      STX &0AF4
806A AD 4B 02  .K.      LDA &024B
806D 8D FE 0A  ...      STA &0AFE
8070 50 2D     P-       BVC &809F
8072 C9 04     ..       CMP #&04
8074 D0 29     .)       BNE &809F
8076 86 4F     .0       STX &4F
8078 20 A2 81  ..       JSR &81A2
807B B0 22     ."       BCS &809F
807D 48        H        PHA
807E 98        .        TYA
807F 48        H        PHA
8080 8A        .        TXA
8081 48        H        PHA
8082 A9 75     .u       LDA #&75
8084 20 F4 FF  ..       JSR &FFF4
8087 86 4E     .N       STX &4E
8089 68        h        PLA
808A AA        .        TAX
808B 68        h        PLA
808C A8        .        TAY
808D 68        h        PLA
808E 20 DB 81  ..       JSR &81DB
8091 A0 0F     ..       LDY #&0F
8093 A5 4E     .N       LDA &4E
8095 29 04     ).       AND #&04
8097 F0 02     ..       BEQ &809B
8099 A0 0E     ..       LDY #&0E
809B 98        .        TYA
809C 20 EE FF  ..       JSR &FFEE
809F A2 00     ..       LDX #&00
80A1 68        h        PLA
80A2 95 4E     .N       STA &4E,X
80A4 E8        .        INX
80A5 E0 0A     ..       CPX #&0A
80A7 90 FB     ..       BCC &80A1
80A9 68        h        PLA
80AA 85 1A     ..       STA &1A
80AC 68        h        PLA
80AD 85 19     ..       STA &19
80AF 68        h        PLA
80B0 8D 02 02  ...      STA &0202
80B3 68        h        PLA
80B4 8D 03 02  ...      STA &0203
80B7 68        h        PLA
80B8 A8        .        TAY
80B9 68        h        PLA
80BA AA        .        TAX
```

```
80BB 68          h      PLA
80BC 60          `      RTS
80BD F0 08       ..     BEQ &80C7
80BF 20 EA 80    ..     JSR &80EA
80C2 20 E0 9C    ..     JSR &9CE0
80C5 50 28       P(     BVC &80EF
80C7 86 4F       .O     STX &4F
80C9 20 3C 9D    <.     JSR &9D3C
80CC D0 2B       .+     BNE &80F9
80CE 20 BF 80    ..     JSR &80BF
80D1 20 E7 FF    ..     JSR &FFE7
80D4 20 E0 9C    ..     JSR &9CE0
80D7 20 E0 9C    ..     JSR &9CE0
80DA 20 ED 80    ..     JSR &80ED
80DD 20 6B 9F    k.     JSR &9F6B
80E0 20 20 49    I      JSR &4920
80E3 4E 46 4F    NFO    LSR &4F46
80E6 0D EA 50    ..P    ORA &50EA
80E9 B5 20       .      LDA &20,X
80EB E7          .      ???
80EC FF          .      ???
80ED A2 FF       ..     LDX #&FF
80EF E8          .      INX
80F0 BD 09 80    ...    LDA &8009,X
80F3 20 EE FF    ..     JSR &FFEE
80F6 D0 F7       ..     BNE &80EF
80F8 60          `      RTS
80F9 20 A2 81    ..     JSR &81A2
80FC C9 FF       ..     CMP #&FF
80FE D0 08       ..     BNE &8108
8100 20 1F 81    ..     JSR &811F
8103 20 E7 FF    ..     JSR &FFE7
8106 50 0B       P.     BVC &8113
8108 C9 FE       ..     CMP #&FE
810A D0 07       ..     BNE &8113
810C 98          .      TYA
810D 48          H      PHA
810E 20 69 82    i.     JSR &8269
8111 68          h      PLA
8112 A8          .      TAY
8113 20 47 9D    G.     JSR &9D47
8116 B0 D0       ..     BCS &80E8
8118 20 3C 9D    <.     JSR &9D3C
811B F0 CB       ..     BEQ &80E8
811D D0 DA       ..     BNE &80F9
811F 20 BF 80    ..     JSR &80BF
8122 A9 EA       ..     LDA #&EA
8124 85 50       .P     STA &50
8126 A9 81       ..     LDA #&81
8128 85 51       .Q     STA &51
```

```
812A A9 5A    .Z    LDA #&5A
812C 85 52    .R    STA &52
812E A9 82    ..    LDA #&82
8130 85 53    .S    STA &53
8132 30 16    0.    BMI &814A
8134 98       .     TYA
8135 48       H     PHA
8136 A9 86    ..    LDA #&86
8138 20 F4 FF ..    JSR &FFF4
813B E0 12    ..    CPX #&12
813D B0 09    ..    BCS &8148
813F A9 12    ..    LDA #&12
8141 20 29 9D ).    JSR &9D29
8144 68       h     PLA
8145 A8       .     TAY
8146 50 0A    P.    BVC &8152
8148 68       h     PLA
8149 A8       .     TAY
814A 20 E7 FF ..    JSR &FFE7
814D A2 02    ..    LDX #&02
814F 20 49 92 I.    JSR &9249
8152 20 EC 9D ..    JSR &9DEC
8155 B0 2F    ./    BCS &8186
8157 09 00    ..    ORA #&00
8159 30 2D    0-    BMI &8188
815B 20 E3 FF ..    JSR &FFE3
815E C9 0D    ..    CMP #&0D
8160 D0 F0    ..    BNE &8152
8162 A2 04    ..    LDX #&04
8164 20 49 92 I.    JSR &9249
8167 EE FB 0A ...   INC &0AFB
816A A9 86    ..    LDA #&86
816C 20 EA 9C ..    JSR &9CEA
816F AD FB 0A ...   LDA &0AFB
8172 C9 31    .1    CMP #&31
8174 90 DC    ..    BCC &8152
8176 C9 3A    .:    CMP #&3A
8178 90 04    ..    BCC &817E
817A D0 D6    ..    BNE &8152
817C 29 30    )0    AND #&30
817E 20 EE FF ..    JSR &FFEE
8181 20 E8 9C ..    JSR &9CE8
8184 50 CC    P.    BVC &8152
8186 38       8     SEC
8187 60       `     RTS
8188 20 EC 9D ..    JSR &9DEC
818B 50 A7    P.    BVC &8134
818D E8       .     INX
818E BD EA 81 ...   LDA &81EA,X
8191 10 FA    ..    BPL &818D
```

```
8193 E8            .     INX
8194 E8            .     INX
8195 A9 00         ..    LDA #&00
8197 E0 80         ..    CPX #&80
8199 B0 EB         ..    BCS &8186
819B A4 57         .W    LDY &57
819D 86 56         .V    STX &56
819F CA            .     DEX
81A0 D0 15         ..    BNE &81B7
81A2 A9 00         ..    LDA #&00
81A4 85 56         .V    STA &56
81A6 B1 19         ..    LDA (&19),Y
81A8 29 DF         ).    AND #&DF
81AA C9 42         .B    CMP #&42
81AC D0 04         ..    BNE &81B2
81AE C8            .     INY
81AF 20 3C 9D      <.    JSR &9D3C
81B2 A2 FF         ..    LDX #&FF
81B4 88            .     DEY
81B5 84 57         .W    STY &57
81B7 C8            .     INY
81B8 E8            .     INX
81B9 BD EA 81      ...   LDA &81EA,X
81BC 30 1A         0.    BMI &81D8
81BE B1 19         ..    LDA (&19),Y
81C0 29 DF         ).    AND #&DF
81C2 DD EA 81      ...   CMP &81EA,X
81C5 F0 F0         ..    BEQ &81B7
81C7 E4 56         .V    CPX &56
81C9 F0 C2         ..    BEQ &818D
81CB B1 19         ..    LDA (&19),Y
81CD C9 2E         ..    CMP #&2E
81CF D0 BC         ..    BNE &818D
81D1 C8            .     INY
81D2 E8            .     INX
81D3 BD EA 81·     ...   LDA &81EA,X
81D6 10 FA         ..    BPL &81D2
81D8 C9 FE         ..    CMP #&FE
81DA 60            '     RTS
81DB 48            H     PHA
81DC BD EB 81      ...   LDA &81EB,X
81DF 48            H     PHA
81E0 A6 4F         .O    LDX &4F
81E2 A9 00         ..    LDA #&00
81E4 9D 13 01      ...   STA &0113,X
81E7 4C 5E 9C      L^.   JMP &9C5E
81EA 43            C     ???
81EB 48            H     PHA
81EC 45 43         EC    EOR &43
81EE 4B            K     ???
```

```
81EF 95 DB     ..    STA &DB,X
81F1 43        C     ???
81F2 4C 45 41  LEA   JMP &4145
81F5 52        R     ???
81F6 9F        .     ???
```

Fig. 7.1. The TOOLKIT interpreter disassembled.

The header and byte usage

As with all sideways ROMs, the front end of the TOOLKIT ROM is occupied by the ROM header, which is 37 bytes long in this case. The TOOLKIT service entry address is &8025. The byte at &8006 gives the ROM type as &82. At bit level, this comes out as 10000010 denoting that the ROM has a service entry, no language entry and no second processor relocation address. The next byte at &8007 gives the copyright offset pointer as &15; thus the copyright string can be accessed by loading this byte into the Y register and peeking the ROM through a vectored address containing &8000.

The TOOLKIT title string includes an ASCII version number. Discounting the BRKs the entire string is:

TOOLKIT 1.22

The final bytes of the ROM header hold the copyright string which is:

(C) 1983 Beebug

The complete ROM header is detailed in Fig. 7.2.

8000	No language entry
8003	Service entry point JMP &8025
8006	ROM type = &82
8007	Copyright offset pointer =&15
8008	BRK
8009	Title string = "TOOLKIT"
8010	BRK
8011	Version string = "1.22"
8015	BRK
8016	Copyright string = "(C) 1983 Beebug"
8024	BRK

Fig. 7.2. The TOOLKIT ROM header.

The command table

All utility ROM-based software is composed of routines that carry out a particular task. These routines are, of course, called by typing in an operating system command name. For example, TOOLKIT contains a command that allows the removal of all spaces and REMs from within a program and this is invoked with the command *PACK. To enable TOOLKIT or any ROM for that matter to identify a command it must keep a list of them so that it can compare the current command that requires identification with those in its own list of commands. If it finds after a series of comparisions that the command issued is the same as one in its lists it can extract a suitably stored execution address and perform an indirect jump to the command's coding. If the command is not identified, the interpreter passes the call back to the MOS, which might then offer it to another ROM. The sequence of commands and their execution addresses is known as the *command table*. The TOOLKIT command table is stored in memory from &81EA to &8268 inclusive. Fig. 7.3 lists the command table.

```
81EA : 43 48 45 43 4B 95 DB 43 CHECK..C
81F2 : 4C 45 41 52 9F 39 45 44 LEAR.9ED
81FA : 49 54 8C 5C 46 52 45 45 IT.\FREE
8202 : 93 E7 4D 45 4D 4F 52 59 ..MEMORY
820A : 92 B2 4D 45 52 47 45 95 ..MERGE.
8212 : 13 4D 4F 56 45 93 88 4E .MOVE..N
821A : 45 57 93 C6 4F 46 46 84 EW..OFF.
8222 : 92 4F 4C 44 93 BA 4F 4E .OLD..ON
822A : 84 98 50 41 43 4B 9A 42 ..PACK.B
8232 : 52 45 43 4F 56 45 52 99 RECOVER.
823A : 75 52 45 4E 55 4D 42 45 uRENUMBE
8242 : 52 96 D9 52 45 50 4F 52 R..REPOR
824A : 54 84 89 53 43 52 45 45 T..SCREE
8252 : 4E 96 8C 55 54 49 4C 85 N..UTIL.
825A : E1 49 4E 46 4F FE 00 54 .INFO..T
8262 : 4F 4F 4C 4B 49 54 FF 20 OOLKIT.
```

Fig. 7.3. The TOOLKIT command table.

Looking at Fig. 7.3, we can clearly see the ASCII command names down the right-hand side of the listing. You'll notice that they do not require the asterisk to be prefixed to them as this has been passed over by the MOS. In all but the last case, the command TOOLKIT, the ASCII command names are followed by two bytes. These are the command's execution addresses and are listed in Fig. 7.4.

The command table listing (Fig. 7.3) shows that, with the exception of the last two, the commands are stored in alphabetical order. There is no real hard and fast rule that this should be the case. The most efficient way would be to store the commands that are most frequently used first of all and

Command	Execution address
CHECK	&95DB
CLEAR	&9F39
EDIT	&8C5C
FREE	&93E7
MEMORY	&92B2
MERGE	&9513
MOVE	&9388
NEW	&93C6
OFF	&93BA
ON	&8498
PACK	&9A42
RECOVER	&9975
RENUMBER	&96D5
REPORT	&8489
SCREEN	&968C
UTIL	&85E1

Fig. 7.4. Execution addresses of TOOLKIT commands.

leave the ones that will probably be used least of all to the end of the command table. This would simply speed up the overall average execution time of a program or use of immediate commands, though in most instances it will only be by a few microseconds! The TOOLKIT command table is alphabetically arranged so that *HELP TOOLKIT will list the commands in this way. The last two commands in the command table, INFO and TOOLKIT, do not have direct execution addresses within the table; instead, they are marked by the two bytes &FE and &FF respectively. This is because these commands are both associated with a *HELP and are handled by the service call 4 processing by the TOOLKIT interpreter, as we shall see later on.

Byte by byte

Now that we have examined the TOOLKIT command table and memory usage we can have a detailed look at the interpreter proper and see just how it works.

The TOOLKIT ROM is entered at the service entry point which performs an immediate jump to the beginning of the interpreter at &8025. As the processor registers convey all information regarding the service call type it is important that they are preserved for future restoration should the service call not be serviced. The code from &8025 to &8029 performs this pushing of accumulator, X register and then Y register onto the hardware stack.

8025	48	H	PHA	push accumulator
8026	8A	.	TXA	move X across
8027	48	H	PHA	and push
8028	98	.	TYA	move Y across
8029	48	H	PHA	and push

The next stage is to preserve the contents of the break vector, BRKV, located at &202 and &203. Again, these bytes go onto the hardware stack.

802A	AD	03	02	...	LDA &0203	get high byte
802D	48			H	PHA	and push
802E	AD	02	02	...	LDA &0202	get low byte
8031	48			H	PHA	and push

As it is possible that the current service call will not be serviced by the TOOLKIT ROM, the BASIC text pointer must be preserved. This can be pushed onto the hardware stack. We must also preserve the operating system text pointer. As the interpreter needs to use this at some point this can be copied into the now 'empty' secondary BASIC text pointer at &19.

8032	A5	19	..	LDA &19	get secondary BASIC text pointer
8034	48		H	PHA	push low byte
8035	A5	1A	..	LDA &1A	and get high byte
8037	48		H	PHA	and push this too
8038	A5	F2	..	LDA &F2	get MOS text pointer
803A	85	19	..	STA &19	seed into BASIC text pointer
803C	A5	F3	..	LDA &F3	get MOS high byte
803E	85	1A	..	STA &1A	and store

As the initial service call processing requires TOOLKIT to use some zero page locations, it is necessary to preserve the contents of the workspace should the service call not be a TOOLKIT one. Ten bytes are required from &4E to &57 inclusive. These bytes are pushed onto the hardware stack by the following loop:

8040	A2	09	..	LDX #&09	ten bytes to move
8042	B5	4E	.N	LDA &4E,X	get byte at &4E+X
8044	48		H	PHA	push on stack
8045	CA		.	DEX	decrement index
8046	10	FA	..	BPL &8042	do until X < 0

Figure 7.5 shows the position of the pushed bytes on the hardware stack at this stage.

To process the service call, the service call number must be recovered.

Stack pointer

RTS	FF
ADDRESS	FE
Accumulator	FC
X Register	FB
Y Register	FA
&203	F9
&202	F8
&19	F7
&1A	F6
&57	F5
&56	F4
&55	F3
&54	F2
&53	F1
&52	F0
&51	EF
&50	EE
&4F	ED
&4E	EC

Fig. 7.5. The workspace saved on the stack.

This has been pushed onto the stack already and can be recovered by moving the stack pointer into the index register and using this as an index from a base address of &111. As the X register holds &EC at this point the address of the byte is &1FC.

The CLV ensures that BVC can be used as an unconditional jump throughout.

8048	BA		.	TSX	move stack pointer into X
8049	BD	11 01	...	LDA &0111,X	get service call type
804C	CA		.	DEX	decrement X by two
804D	CA		.	DEX	
804E	B8		.	CLV	clear overflow flag

We can now test for the service call type. *HELP is tested for first of all. If the service type is 9 then a branch to &80BD is performed. This, in fact, invokes another branch to overcome the limited branch distance, and the final destination for the service type 9 is &80C7.

| 804F | C9 | 09 | .. | CMP #&09 | is it *HELP? |
| 8051 | F0 | 6A | .j | BEQ &80BD | branch if yes |

The next service type tested for is code 1, an absolute service call claim. In fact, TOOLKIT has no need to claim any static workspace, but this call is trapped by the interpreter to allow the ROM to initialise various bytes. If the service type is not 1, then a branch to &8072 is performed, else the X register is cleared and stored in &08 and &09 to reset ERL as BASIC does not do this on BREAK. The bytes at &AF6, &AF5 and &AFF are also cleared. The former two bytes are associated with the first search line number used by *UTIL 1 and *UTIL 2. The byte at &AFF is the 'on' flag. The X register is decremented to &FF which is then poked in the byte at &AF4.

The byte at &245 is used by the MOS to indicate just which sideways ROM socket contains BASIC, and a copy of this is made to &AFE for use by the TOOLKIT *REPORT command. At this stage TOOLKIT has performed all it needs to, so a forced branch to &809F is made making use of the clear overflow flag, enabling workspace and variables to be restored and a return to the MOS performed.

8053	C9	01		..	CMP #&01	is it absolute workspace claim?
8055	D0	1B		..	BNE &8072	if not branch
8057	A2	00		..	LDX #&00	clear X register
8059	86	08		..	STX &08	and reset ERL
805B	86	09		..	STX &09	
805D	8E	F5	0A	...	STX &0AF5	and first line number as
8060	8E	F6	0A	...	STX &0AF6	used by *UTIL 1/2
8063	8E	FF	0A	...	STX &0AFF	clear on flag
8066	CA			.	DEX	get &FF into X register
8067	8E	F4	0A	...	STX &0AF4	save as high byte line number for UTIL 1/2
806A	AD	4B	02	.K.	LDA &024B	get BASIC ROM identity
806D	8D	FE	0A	...	STA &0AFE	and save it for use by *REPORT
8070	50	2D		P-	BVC &809F	force branch to restore and return

The final service call type test made by the TOOLKIT interpreter is that of service type 4, test for unknown command. If the accumulator does not hold 4, then a branch to &809F is executed. If the call is 4, then the X register contents, the stack pointer −2, are saved in &4F. A jump to the command identifying routine at &81A2 is then performed.

8072	C9	04		..	CMP #&04	is it unknown command?
8074	D0	29		.)	BNE &809F	if not then branch to &809F
8076	86	4F		.O	STX &4F	save stack pointer
8078	20	A2	81	..	JSR &81A2	and try to identify command

On return from the command identifying subroutine call, the carry flag will be set if the command was not found in the TOOLKIT command table. Thus, a simple BCS can be performed to branch to the TOOLKIT exit service call coding.

807B	B0	22		."	BCS &809F	branch out if carry is set

If the command has been found within the command table then the three main processor registers are saved onto the hardware stack and an OSBYTE &75 call performed to read the VDU status. This allows the screen's paged mode status to be restored on completion, if altered by the command. The status byte is returned in the X register so this is saved at &4E before the processor registers are pulled back from the stack.

807D	48			H	PHA	save accumulator
807E	98			.	TYA	move Y across
807F	48			H	PHA	and push
8080	8A			.	TXA	move X across
8081	48			H	PHA	and push
8082	A9	75		.u	LDA #&75	do OSBYTE and read
8084	20	F4	FF	..	JSR &FFF4	current VDU status
8087	86	4E		.N	STX &4E	save VDU status
8089	68			h	PLA	pull X register
808A	AA			.	TAX	and move across
808B	68			h	PLA	pull Y register
808C	A8			.	TAY	and move across
808D	68			h	PLA	pull accumulator

Now the registers are restored the execution address of the identified command can be peeked. The two-byte address is then pushed onto the hardware stack and the accumulator position on the stack overwritten with a zero so that on being restored it will indicate that the service call has been completed by the TOOLKIT ROM.

At this point, the subroutine performs another jump to code beginning at &9C5E which, among a variety of other things, copies some code from within the TOOLKIT ROM into memory from &A00. This is important as TOOLKIT needs to be able to work with both versions of BASIC (i.e. BASIC I and BASIC II). By ascertaining which BASIC is in use, the interpreter can write appropriate addresses into the RAM-based code so that it can be executed correctly. While nested in this routine, the execution address is pulled from the stack so that the program flow simply returns to the execution address. Later the command itself returns with an RTS to &8091.

808E	20	DB	81	..	JSR &81DB	get address and push onto stack

The next bytes of coding deal with the previously read VDU status, in an effort to find out the paged mode status of the Beeb. The coding begins by loading &0F into the Y register. &0F is the ASCII code issued to put the micro in the normal scroll, non-paged mode. The previously read VDU status is then loaded into the accumulator and bit 2 preserved by logically ANDing the accumulator with 4, 00000100 binary. This bit is set if scrolling is selected and a branch to &809B is performed. If paged mode is on then the VDU code &0E is loaded into the Y register. The two possible coding routes rejoin at &809B and the preserved paged mode status transferred across into the accumulator and printed by calling OSWRCH.

8091	A0	0F		..	LDY #&0F	get scrolling mode code into Y
8093	A5	4E		.N	LDA &4E	get VDU status byte
8095	29	04		).	AND #&04	is bit set?
8097	F0	02		..	BEQ &809B	branch if not
8099	A0	0E		..	LDY #&0E	if set get paged mode on code
809B	98			.	TYA	move code into accumulator
809C	20	EE	FF	..	JSR &FFEE	and print it

This point now marks the TOOLKIT service entry exit procedure. If the service call type was not recognised then this is the entry point after the last service call test at &8072. It is also the final procedure after executing the command, should it have been identified as a TOOLKIT command.

The first thing to do is to restore the TOOLKIT workspace to its original contents. A simple loop is used to pull and store the previously pushed 10 bytes.

809F	A2	00		..	LDX #&00	initialise index
80A1	68			h	PLA	pull stack
80A2	95	4E		.N	STA &4E,X	place in zero page at &4E+X
80A4	E8			.	INX	increment index
80A5	E0	0A		..	CPX #&0A	compare with 10
80A7	90	F8		..	BCC &80A1	and repeat loop until all 10 done

The next two stages involve restoring the contents of the secondary BASIC text pointer and BRKV. They simply need to be pulled from the hardware stack and stored appropriately.

80A9 68		h	PLA	get high byte BASIC text pointer
80AA 85	1A	..	STA&1A	store it in vector
80AC 68		h	PLA	get low byte of same
80AD 85	19	..	STA&19	and store in vector
80AF 68		h	PLA	get low byte of BRKV
80B0 8D	02 02	...	STA&0202	store in vector
80B3 68		h	PLA	and get high byte of same
80B4 8D	03 02	...	STA&0203	and store

The penultimate act is to restore the entry values of the processor registers which were pushed onto the stack as the first act of the TOOLKIT interpreter. The final instruction in the interpreter flow is the RTS to return control to the MOS.

80B7 68		h	PLA	pull Y from stack
80B8 A8		.	TAY	move across
80B9 68		h	PLA	pull X from stack
80BA AA		.	TAX	move across
80BB 68		h	PLA	pull service call
80BC 60		.	RTS	and pack to MOS

The subroutines

Having completed the main interpreter loop, we shall now look at the workings of the subroutines called by the TOOLKIT interpreter.

The first operation outside the main interpreter is the branch for a *HELP service call. This simply performs a further branch to &80C7 – remember, the zero flag will be clear after the CMP #&09 instruction.

80BD F0	08	..	BEQ&80C7	force branch to &80C7

The next bytes of coding are not executed by the normal 'flow' of the program but are called by the *HELP processing routine to issue the correct sequence of help messages. The JSR &80EA is used to print a new line and the string "TOOLKIT" followed by a space and the version number string.

80BF 20	EA 80	..	JSR&80EA	do OSNEWL and print TOOLKIT
80C2 20	E0 9C	..	JSR &9CE0	print a space
80C5 50	28	P(	BVC &80EF	force branch to print version string

The code starting at &80C7 is the ultimate destination address of the *HELP entry service call. The code commences by saving the X register, which contains the stack pointer at &4F.

The subroutine call to &9D3C tests for the presence of an ASCII return character. This will indicate whether the service call was issued by a simple *HELP or a specific command such as *HELP TOOLKIT. The last instruction of the subroutine tests for a RETURN, so the zero flag will be set if the return character, ASCII &0D, is present. If the return is absent then a branch to &80F9 is performed.

80C7 86	4F		.O	STX &4F	save ROM number
80C9 20	3C	9D	<.	JSR &9D3C	is it simple or specific *HELP?
80CC D0	2B		.+	BNE &80F9	it is specific so branch

If the call is non-specific the call to &80BF will issue a carriage return and print the ASCII string "TOOLKIT 1.22" onto the screen. After a call to OSNEWL two calls to the subroutine at &9CE0 are executed to print padding spaces onto the screen, followed by the subroutine call to &80ED which prints the string "TOOLKIT". The call to &9F6B then prints the ASCII text embedded in the text that follows it until it encounters a negative byte, i.e. a byte which has its most significant bit set. The text can be seen clearly, i.e. INFO and the NOP instruction is the negative byte.

80CE 20	BF	80	..	JSR &80BF	print return and then "TOOLKIT 1.22"
80D1 20	E7	FF	..	JSR &FFE7	print new line
80D4 20	E0	9C	..	JSR &9CE0	print two padding spaces
80D7 20	E0	9C	..	JSR &9CE0	print two padding spaces
80DA 20	ED	80	..	JSR &80ED	print "TOOLKIT"
80DD 20	6B	9F	k.	JSR &9F6B	print "INFO"
80E0 20					ASCII space
80E1 20					ASCII space
80E2 49			I		ASCII I
80E3 4E			N		ASCII N
80E4 46			F		ASCII F
80E5 4F			O		ASCII O
80E6 0D			.		ASCII return
80E7 EA			.	NOP	negative byte

Now that the *HELP call has been processed, the TOOLKIT exit and return to MOS routine can be carried out by a forced branch to the exit coding at &809F.

80E8 50	B5	..P	BVC&809F	force branch to TOOLKIT exit

The address &80EA is the entry point for the subroutine to print the string

```
>*HELP INFO

TOOLKIT 1.21
    FX   3  0              FX   4  0
    FX   5  1              FX   6  10
    FX   9  25             FX  10  25
    FX  11  50             FX  12  8

    @%=&0000090A

    LISTO  0               WIDTH  0
    ERR    0               ERL    0

REPORT:


Free memory = 25342 bytes
Program size=        2 bytes
Next free location= &1902
PAGE= &1900   LOMEM= &1902
TOP = &1902   HIMEM= &7C00

OS 1.20
>_
```

Fig. 7.6. The TOOLKIT *HELP INFO sheet.

"TOOLKIT". After printing a new line by calling OSNEWL the X register is used as an index to access and print the TOOLKIT ASCII string located at &8009.

80EA	20	E7	FF	..	JSR &FFE7	call OSNEWL
80ED	A2	FF		..	LDX #&FF	initialise index register
80EF	E8			.	INX	increment index
80F0	BD	09	80	...	LDA &8009,X	get ASCII byte
80F3	20	EE	FF	..	JSR &FFEE	print it with OSWRCH
80F6	D0	F7		..	BNE &80EF	branch until zero byte encountered
80F8	60			.	RTS	and return from subroutine call

The address &80F9 is the entry point for an unrecognised command service call and also the entry point from the *HELP routine that is issuing a specific *HELP command, i.e. *HELP TOOLKIT. The routine begins by calling the subroutine at &81A2 which compares the unrecognised command with those in the TOOLKIT command table. The two *HELP associated commands are TOOLKIT and INFO; if either of these are identified in the 'compare with command table subroutine' then the accumulator will hold &FF or &FE on return. If &FF is returned then the unrecognised *HELP was *HELP TOOLKIT. This requires the complete list of TOOLKIT commands to be printed out, and this is initialised by a subroutine call to &811F. Upon return, a call to OSNEWL is followed by a forced branch to &8113 which then tests for any further *HELP parameters.

80F9	20	A2	81	..	JSR &81A2	test for command in command table
80FC	C9	FF		..	CMP #&FF	was it TOOLKIT?
80FE	D0	08		..	BNE &8108	branch if not
8100	20	1F	81	..	JSR &811F	if yes print commands in command table
8103	20	E7	FF	..	JSR &FFE7	call OSNEWL
8106	50	0B		P.	BVC &8113	force branch

If the accumulator returns &FE then a *HELP INFO has been detected by the interpreter. A subroutine jump to &8269 executes the *HELP INFO command and program and operating system details are printed to the screen. On return, a test is made for any further *HELP parameters. Note that the Y register which holds the offset into the *HELP command line is preserved and restored as need be using the hardware stack, so that the current command line position is not lost.

8108	C9	FE		..	CMP #&FE	was it *HELP INFO?
810A	D0	07		..	BNE &8113	branch if not
810C	98			.	TYA	save index
810D	48			H	PHA	by pushing onto stack
810E	20	69	82	i.	JSR &8269	execute INFO
8111	68			h	PLA	pull stack
8112	A8			.	TAY	and restore index
8113	20	47	9D	G.	JSR &9D47	move past other characters to next space or RETURN
8116	B0	D0		..	BCS &80E8	if RETURN present carry is set so branch and exit
8118	20	3C	9D	<.	JSR &9D3C	move past spaces and test for RETURN
811B	F0	CB		..	BEQ &80E8	if RETURN branch and exit
811D	D0	DA		..	BNE &80F9	else test command table for next *HELP command

The next section of code marks the entry for the routine to print the TOOLKIT commands after a *HELP TOOLKIT command has been identified. The subroutine at &80EF is used to print the TOOLKIT string. The start and end addresses of the command table are then seeded into two vectors located in zero page at &50 and &52. These are the start and end addresses of the commands in the command table (refer back to Fig. 7.3). As the last byte loaded into the accumulator at &812E was a negative byte, the BMI at &8132 to &814A is forced.

811F	20	BF	80	..	JSR &80BF	print TOOLKIT
8122	A9	EA		..	LDA #&EA	low byte address of CT
8124	85	50		.P	STA &50	store in vector
8126	A9	81		..	LDA #&81	high byte of same address
8128	85	51		.Q	STA &51	store in vector
812A	A9	5A		.Z	LDA #&5A	low byte address of byte after last command in CT
812C	85	52		.R	STA &52	store in vector
812E	A9	82		..	LDA #&82	high byte of same
8130	85	53		.S	STA &53	store in vector
8132	30	16		0.	BMI &814A	negative flag set so force branch

The following sections of the interpreter are all concerned with the action of the command table against unrecognised command testing sequence. The bytes from &818D to &8194 are responsible for moving through the command table until the next command in it is reached. If the current command under test is dissimilar to the one that initiated the service call then the next command in the command table must be tested. You will remember that the command table is arranged with the command in ASCII form followed by its two-byte execution address, high byte first as illustrated in Fig. 7.3. As the execution addresses will always be greater than &8000, the first byte will be negative in two's complement form and therefore if this byte is loaded into a register the negative flag of the status register will be set. This fact can be used to control the 'moving on' loop.

The X register is used as the index into the command table which starts at &81EA. The index is incremented and the next byte loaded into the accumulator. If the byte is an ASCII code the negative flag will be clear and the BPL at &8091 performed to reiterate the loop. On the other hand, the negative flag will be set if the index now points at the high byte address and the branch will not occur. To move past the two-byte address and point to the next command in the table, the index register is incremented by two.

818D	E8			.	INX	increment index
818E	BD	EA	81	...	LDA &81EA,X	get byte from command table
8191	10	FA		..	BPL &818D	redo if ASCII
8193	E8			.	INX	else move past two-byte address
8194	E8			.	INX	

Of course, a test must be performed to see if the end of the command table has been reached and that is done next. The accumulator is loaded with zero to clear the zero flag and the X register contents are then compared with

#&80, which would place the index at &826A, two bytes past the last command in the command table. This comparison would leave the carry flag set and a branch to &8186 effected. This leaves the carry flag set and indicates to the calling routine in the main section of the interpreter that the unrecognised command was not found in the command table.

8195	A9	00	..	LDA #&00	clear accumulator
8197	E0	80	..	CPX #&80	is index less than 128?
8199	B0	EB	..	BCS &8186	if not branch

The next command in the command table can now be compared with the unrecognised command. The Y register, the index which marks the first byte in the unrecognised command, is reloaded from its temporary store at &57 with the index into the command table saved in the preceding location, &56. The X register is then decremented to allow for the INX at &8188 so that a forced branch can be effected to &81B7 to skip over the subroutine's entry point and therefore the set-up coding.

819B	A4	57	.W	LDY &57	get index into command
819D	86	56	.V	STX &56	save index into command table
819F	CA		.	DEX	condition zero flag
81A0	D0	15	..	BNE &81B7	and force a branch

&81A2 is the entry point called by the interpreter at &80F9 to identify an unrecognised command. The accumulator is first loaded with zero and stored at &56 which is the command table offset byte storage used by the X register. The vectored address at &19 holds the MOS text pointer, which gives the start address of the unrecognised command. Using post-indirect addressing, the first byte of the unrecognised command is loaded into the accumulator. This, in turn, is logically ANDed with &DF, which has the effect of forcing the byte to upper-case. Thus, if the byte were lower-case ASCII, it would now be upper-case ASCII. At bit level, the difference between upper-case ASCII characters and their lower-case counterparts is the state of bit 5. For example:

ASC"B" = &42 = 01000010
ASC"b" = &62 = 01100010

Setting or clearing bit 5 will toggle the case of the ASCII code. If the accumulator holds &62 and this is logically ANDed with &DF, we get:

$$\begin{array}{rcl} \text{ASC"b"} = \&62 &=& 01100010 \\ \&DF &=& \underline{11011111} \\ && 01000010 \end{array}$$

The binary result is &42, which is ASC"B".

The example character used above, B, was deliberate. There is a large quantity of sideways ROMs available now and inevitably there will be ROMs that use similar commands. If, in normal circumstances, one of these commands is issued, the sideways ROM with the higher priority will execute the command. TOOLKIT circumvents this by allowing the programmer to prefix any of its commands with a B to select them. Thus, BCHECK and bCHECK will ensure that TOOLKIT's CHECK command is executed! The test for the prefixed B is made in the comparison at &81B2. If the B is absent then a branch to &81B2 is performed.

81A2	A9	00		..	LDA #&00	clear accumulator
81A4	85	56		.V	STA &56	and command table index
81A6	B1	19		..	LDA (&19),Y	get first byte of
						unrecognised command
81A8	29	DF		).	AND #&DF	force byte to upper-case
81AA	C9	42		.B	CMP #&42	is it 'B'?
81AC	D0	04		..	BNE &81B2	branch if not

If the byte is B then the command index is incremented and a subroutine call to &9D3C performed to move past any spaces.

81AE	C8			.	INY	increment index
81AF	20	3C	9D	<.	JSR &9D3C	move past any spaces

After loading &FF into the X register, Y is decremented and saved in its temporary storage byte at &57. Both of these registers are set to hold one byte less than they actually need as the loop the subroutine is about to enter begins by incrementing them both!

81B2	A2	FF		..	LDX #&FF	load &FF into X register
81B4	88			.	DEY	decrement post-
						indexing index
81B5	84	57		.W	STY &57	and save
81B7	C8			.	INY	increment Y
81BB	E8			.	INX	increment X

The next area of machine code controls the comparison of unrecognised command with each of those in the TOOLKIT command table. A byte is first loaded into the accumulator from the command table. If this is a negative byte, and therefore an address byte, the end of the command has been reached and therefore identified. If this is the case a branch to &81D8 is executed. If this is not the case a byte from the unrecognised command string is loaded into the accumulator and forced to upper-case. This process shows that all TOOLKIT commands can be typed in as either upper- or lower-case characters. This byte is then compared with the corresponding byte in the command table. If the bytes are the same, the branch to &81B7 is performed to move to the next character in the buffer.

81B9	BD	EA	81	...	LDA&81EA,X	get byte from command table
81BC	30	1A		0.	BMI&81D8	branch out if address byte
81BE	B1	19		..	LDA(&19),Y	get byte from unrecognised command
81C0	29	DF		).	AND #&DF	force it to upper-case
81C2	DD	EA	81	...	CMP&81EA,X	compare with byte in command table
81C5	F0	F0		..	BEQ&81B7	branch if they are the same

The X register is then compared with the contents of its starting value held in &56. If these are the same then the character just tested was the first in the command. Therefore the two commands being compared must be different, and the branch to &818D performed to move onto the next command in the command table. This is also to prevent *. from being accepted as a TOOLKIT command!

| 81C7 | E4 | 56 | | .V | CPX&56 | is X equal to contents of &56 |
| 81C9 | F0 | C2 | | .. | BEQ&818D | branch if yes |

It is possible that an abbreviation of the command has been used, i.e. *CH. in place of *CHECK; as TOOLKIT allows abbreviations of commands, this must be tested. To do this the unrecognised byte in the unrecognised command is reloaded into the accumulator and compared with ASC".". If the byte is not a full-stop then a branch to &818D is performed to move to the next command in the command table.

81CB	B1	19		..	LDA(&19),Y	get unrecognised byte
81CD	C9	2E		..	CMP #&2E	is it ASC"."?
81CF	D0	BC		..	BNE &818D	branch if not

If this point is reached then the command has been recognised as an abbreviated one. The next step is to access its execution address. This is done by incrementing the X register and loading bytes into the accumulator until a negative byte is encountered.

81D1	C8			.	INY	increment post index
81D2	E8			.	INX	increment command table index
81D3	BD	EA	81	...	LDA&81EA,X	get byte from command table
81D6	10	FA		..	BPL&81D2	branch until negative

The final act of this subroutine is to compare the negative byte in the accumulator with the *INFO flag before returning.

| 81D8 | C9 | FE | | .. | CMP #&FE | is it *INFO? |
| 81DA | 60 | | | . | RTS | return to main coding |

At your service!

After a command has been identified, the execution address must be extracted and the service call type on the stack must be replaced with &00 to indicate to the MOS that the service has indeed been performed. Fifteen bytes starting at &81DB invoke this. On entry to this section of the subroutine, the accumulator holds the high byte of the execution address; this is pushed onto the stack. The X register points at the low byte which is extracted from the command table and pushed onto the stack.

To write &00 into the service call type it is necessary to write directly into the stack. To do this, the stack pointer is obtained from the copy in &4F; the accumulator is loaded with zero, and the service call type overwritten with &00.

The final act is to jump directly to code at &9C5E.

81DB 48			H	PHA	push high byte address
81DC BD	EB	81	...	LDA&81EB,X	get low byte address
81DF 48			H	PHA	and push
81E0 A6	4F		.O	LDX&4F	get stack pointer copy
81E2 A9	00		..	LDA #&00	load accumulator with zero
81E4 9D	13	01	...	STA&0113,X	and write new service code type
81E7 4C	5E	9C	L^.	JMP&9C5E	

The final JMP to &9C5C will eventually return to the action address and, when finished, return to the JSR at &808E.

Chapter Eight
Breaking In

Virtually all sideways ROM software available these days is accessed using an operating system command. However, there are other ways in which sideways ROM- and RAM-based commands may be added, simply by 'trapping' the various errors that the MOS or BASIC would issue when it does not recognise a command. I used the word 'simply' above, but this is really a gross understatement. Trapping errors and processing them correctly is certainly not an easy task, particularly in the machine code required to process them. One sideways ROM that does use this approach is the ADDCOMM toolkit.

ADDCOMM

The ADDCOMM ROM works by trapping the BRK error service call. When BASIC cannot recognise a command it issues an error message. The error message is instigated by a BRK instruction embedded in the BASIC ROM and followed by an ASCII message string which is again terminated by a BRK instruction. Whenever a BRK is encountered the MOS will issue a service call to the sideways ROMs – service call type 6, in fact – so that the service call interpreter of any sideways ROM may test for and trap the BRK error for processing. If no ROM responds to the service call, control is returned to the current language via the BRK vector which should then issue the appropriate error message. Program 8.1 is a simple example of how an error message, or any program end message can be generated using BRK. When the message is printed by BASIC it excludes the first character for some obscure reason (anyone know why?) so an extra space character has been added at the start of the ASCII string in line 100.

When service call 6 is issued, the vectored address in &FD and &FE points to the error message number that caused the BRK. Location &F0 contains a copy of the stack pointer after the BRK was executed. If a sideways ROM issued the error then OSBYTE &BA will return the number of the ROM that was in use when it was issued. Preserving the location of the error number is important as its value will give a good indication as to

```
 10 REM Messages using BRK
 20 REM The BBC Micro ROM Book
 30 REM (c) Bruce Smith October 1984
 40 :
 50 P%=&C00
 60 [.start
 70 LDA #7
 80 JSR &FFE3
 90 BRK
100 EQUS " Bleeping 'ell!"
110 EQUB 13
120 BRK
130 ]
```

Program 8.1. Printing messages with BRK.

exactly what caused the error. Consider the error message "Bad MODE"; it would be pointless for a sideways ROM to go any further in processing this error after intercepting the BRK service as it would obviously never be a command in the ROM. An unrecognised 'word' will cause a 'Mistake' error, error number 4, to be generated. If this is the case the interpreter can then go ahead and test for the command in its command table, otherwise it can simply return control back to the MOS.

The ADDCOMM interpreter

Figure 8.1 flowcharts roughly the major processing carried out by the ADDCOMM interpreter. To begin with, it receives a service call from the MOS and checks to see if it is a BRK service. If not, and it is not a *HELP service, then control is returned to the MOS immediately. If the service call is for BRK processing then the processor registers are pushed onto the hardware stack. Using the vectored address at &FD, the error code is evaluated. If it is not a 'Mistake' error then the processor registers are restored and again a simple RTS returns control back to the MOS. Assuming that the error was a 'Mistake' error then the interpreter must assure itself that it was, in fact, issued by the BASIC chip itself. It's quite possible, though it should not happen, that error 4 could be issued by another sideways ROM. If the error was not generated by the BASIC chip then registers are restored and a return performed.

If this point in the ADDCOMM interpreter has been reached then the error has been trapped. The character string which could be an ADDCOMM command is now pointed to by the vectored address in &B and &C and the offset in location &A. Identifying the 'command' is now possible by comparing the ASCII string with each command in the ADDCOMM command table. If the command is not recognised as an ADDCOMM command the stack is pulled to restore processor registers

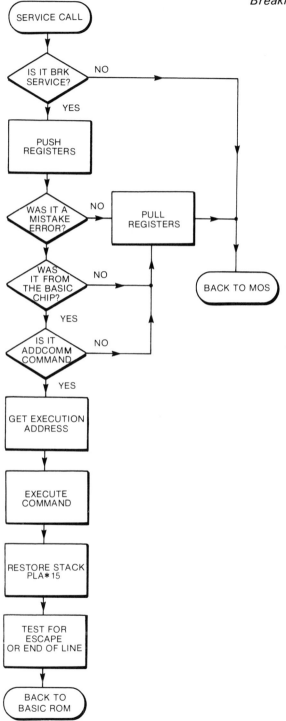

Fig. 8.1. ADDCOMM flowchart.

and an RTS performed. If the command is recognised, its execution address is extracted and jumped to for execution.

After executing the command, control must be handed back to BASIC, but the hardware stack will have become corrupted with extra bytes surplus to requirement. In fact, the stack will hold the fifteen extra bytes. These are the previously pushed processor registers: the initial subroutine call to the ADDCOMM ROM, plus data originally pushed by the MOS prior to the service call. To remove and discard this the stack can be pulled fifteen times!

The ADDCOMM interpreter is now in a position to jump back to BASIC, but this can be a fiddly process. After any command has been executed, the 'end of statement' routine in the BASIC ROM at &9857 (&9810 in BASIC I) must be called. The routine checks for the first non-space character after the ADDCOMM command. This should be either a colon, a carriage return, or an ELSE token. If one of these is detected then all is well, otherwise a 'Syntax error' must be generated. Finally, before returning back to ADDCOMM, this subroutine also checks the escape flag to see if the ESCAPE key has been pressed, thereby generating an 'Escape' error. After returning to ADDCOMM, a jump back into BASIC to address &8B9B (&8B0C in BASIC II) can be performed, and the rest of the program completed.

All this JSRing and JMPing cannot be performed directly, however, simply because the addresses being called are in a different ROM occupying the same space as ADDCOMM. Also, as we have seen, the addresses being called vary depending on whether BASIC I or BASIC II is in use. To overcome this problem, ADDCOMM writes a short section of machine code into its private memory that can be overwritten with the appropriate BASIC addresses and used to jump between the ADDCOMM and BASIC ROMs.

Error sampling

Program 8.1 uses the BRK/Mistake trapping process to add three simple commands to your Beeb's vocabulary. The interpreter is entirely RAM-based and assembles from &A00 or elsewhere if you alter the value initially assigned to P%. The purpose of the program is to show just how it's done, but the program has many drawbacks that would need rectifying before it could be accommodated in a sideways ROM/RAM for effective use. First, the three error statements, REPORT, ERR and ERL will give incorrect results after a command has been executed. Second, the BASIC stack will be corrupted, ultimately resulting in a 'No room' error at some stage. Both of these points would need remedying before even this program could be used effectively.

The program itself works by re-vectoring the BRK vector, BRKV at &202 and pointing it to the RAM-based interpreter. When a BRK occurs, the

MOS will indirect through this vector and execute the code at the address jumped to, i.e. &A00 in this case. At the time of the indirect jump the accumulator and index registers are unchanged from when the BRK was performed. The 6502 hardware stack will be set up for an RTI (Return from Interrupt) to the opcode following the BRK instruction; in other words, the stack will have the status register followed by the return address. On entering the RAM-based interpreter, these bytes can be discarded (lines 410 to 450), because BASIC will reset the stack anyway! Using the BASIC text pointer's vectored address the error number is accessed post-indirectly and tested for a 'Mistake' error (lines 460 to 480). If the error is something different then the BASIC error handler can be jumped to. Now the RAM-based interpreter has trapped the error and can evaluate it against its command table. If the command is recognised then it can be executed by extracing and jumping to its execution address before testing for 'End of statement' and returning to BASIC.

The commands

The three commands added by the RAM-based interpreter are:

    BEEP
    PACK
    TEST

BEEP simply produces a bell character on the internal speaker by executing VDU7; PACK will remove all surplus spaces and REMs from within a program located at PAGE, while leaving spaces within strings and quotes well alone; and TEST will convert the single byte value after the command into an ASCII character printing it to the screen. Thus,

    TEST 65

will print A, as would

    TEST &41.

All three commands can be used freely within programs as they are or as immediate commands directly at the keyboard. The machine code associated with PACK is borrowed from my other book, *The BBC Micro Machine Code Portfolio* which contains 75 machine code programs, many of which would be suitable for incorporating in sideways ROM or RAM.

Before testing the interpreter it is well worth saving it *before* using it! This should come naturally to you, anyway, as it is always advisable to do this before calling any machine code. If an error is made in entering the coding for PACK it would corrupt the whole program. You have been warned!

Remember that pressing the BREAK key will reset the BRKV to its more usual value – so you would need to re-RUN the program to reset the vector or simply poke the correct bytes into the vector, such as:

?&202=0:?&203=&A

The BRK Interpreter

```
  10 REM Trapping BRK and 'Mistake'
  20 REM The BBC Micro ROM Book
  30 REM (c) Bruce Smith October 1984
  40 REM Thanks to Richard Mallette
  50 REM Author of ADDCOMM by Vine Micr
os
  60 :
  70 IF ?&203 < &80 PRINT"Extended Basi
c Installed": VDU 7 : END
  80 old_vector=!&202 AND &FFFF
  81 current=&37
  82 new_position=&39
  83 rem_flag=&45
  90 IF ?&8015=ASC"1" THEN PROCone ELSE
 PROCtwo
 100 PROCassemble
 110 !&202=(!&202 AND &FFFF0000)+start
 120 CLS
 130 PRINT"Extended Basic V1 Installed"

 140 END
 150 DEF PROCone
 160 chkend=&9810
 170 contbasic=&8B0C
 180 evaluate=&87E4
 190 ENDPROC
 200 :
 210 DEF PROCtwo
 220 chkend=&9857
 230 contbasic=&8B9B
 240 evaluate=&8821
 250 ENDPROC
 260 :
 270 DEF PROCassemble
 280 FOR pass=0 TO 3 STEP 3
 290 P%=&900
 300 [OPT pass
 310 .ignore
 320 JMP old_vector
 330 .start
 340 PLA
 350 PLA
```

```
360 PLA
370 PLA
380 PLA
390 LDY #0
400 LDA (&FD),Y
410 CMP #4
420 BNE ignore
430 DEC &A
440 LDA &A
450 CLC
460 ADC &B
470 STA &B
480 BCC skip_1
490 INC &C
500 .skip_1
510 LDA #command_table DIV 256
520 STA &1A
530 LDA #command_table MOD 256
540 STA &19
550 STA &A
560 .interpret
570 LDY #&FF
580 .interpret_loop
590 INY
600 LDA (&19),Y
610 BEQ found_it
620 CMP #&FF
630 BEQ ignore
640 CMP (&B),Y
650 BNE next_try
660 BEQ interpret_loop
670 .found_it
680 STY &A
690 INY
700 LDA (&19),Y
710 STA &37
720 INY
730 LDA (&19),Y
740 STA &38
750 JMP (&37)
760 .next_try
770 INY
780 LDA (&19),Y
790 BNE next_try
800 INY
810 INY
820 INY
830 CLC
840 TYA
850 ADC &19
```

```
 860 STA &19
 870 BCC skip_2
 880 INC &1A
 890 .skip_2
 900 JMP interpret
 910 .endcomm
 920 JSR chkend
 930 JMP contbasic
 940 .command_table
 950 EQUS "PACK"
 960 EQUB 0
 970 EQUW pack
 980 EQUS "TEST"
 990 EQUB 0
1000 EQUW test
1010 EQUS "BEEP"
1020 EQUB 0
1030 EQUW beep
1040 EQUB &FF
1050 .pack
1060 LDA #0
1070 STA new_position
1080 STA current
1090 LDA &18
1100 STA new_position+1
1110 STA current+1
1120 .outer
1130 LDA #0
1140 STA rem_flag
1150 LDY #1
1160 JSR transfer
1170 CMP #&FF
1180 BEQ all_done
1190 JSR transfer
1200 JSR transfer
1210 .inner
1220 LDA (current),Y
1230 BIT rem_flag
1240 BPL flag_clear
1250 CMP #13
1260 BNE space
1270 JSR transfer
1280 BEQ end_of_line
1290 .flag_clear
1300 CMP #ASC" "
1310 BEQ space'
1320  CMP #&F4
1330 BNE not_rem
1340 DEY
1350 LDA #&FF
```

```
1360 STA rem_flag
1370 BNE space
1380 .not_rem
1390 JSR transfer
1400 BEQ end_of_line
1410 CMP #&22
1420 BEQ inside_quote
1430 BNE inner
1440 .space
1450 INC current
1460 BNE inner
1470 INC current+1
1480 BNE inner
1490 .end_of_line
1500 DEY
1510 TYA
1520 PHA
1530 CPY #3
1540 BEQ clear
1550 LDY #3
1560 STA (new_position),Y
1570 CLC
1580 ADC new_position
1590 STA new_position
1600 BCC clear
1610 INC new_position+1
1620 .clear
1630 PLA
1640 CLC
1650 ADC current
1660 STA current
1670 BCC outer
1680 INC current+1
1690 BNE outer
1700 .inside_quote
1710 JSR transfer
1720 BEQ end_of_line
1730 CMP #&22
1740 BNE inside_quote
1750 BEQ inner
1760 .all_done
1770 LDA new_position
1780 CLC
1790 ADC #2
1800 STA &12
1810 LDA new_position+1
1820 ADC #0
1830 STA &13
1840 JMP endcomm
1850 .transfer
```

```
1860 LDA (current),Y
1870 STA (new_position),Y
1880 INY
1890 CMP #13
1900 RTS
1910 .get_number
1920 JMP evaluate
1930 .test
1940 JSR get_number
1950 LDA &2A
1960 JSR &FFEE
1970 JMP endcomm
1980 .beep
1990 LDA #7
2000 JSR &FFEE
2010 JMP endcomm
2020 ]
2030 NEXT
2040 ENDPROC
```

Program 8.2. The BRK interpreter.

Line by line

A line by line description of Program 8.2, the BRK/Mistake interpreter, now follows.

Line 110: If extended BASIC is already installed, inform user.

Line 120: Get address of normal BASIC error handler.

Lines 130 to 150: Set up zero page storage.

Line 160: Check for BASIC version and assigned correct addresses to relevant variables.

Line 170: Assemble machine code.

Lines 180 to 200: Re-vector BRKV and inform user that extended BASIC is now installed.

Lines 220 to 260: Procedure to assign variables BASIC I addresses.

Lines 280 to 320: Procedure to assign variables BASIC II addresses.

Line 380: Entry point for jumps or branches to 'ignore'.

Line 390: Return control to BASIC error handler.

Line 400: Entry address pointed to by BRKV.

Lines 410 to 450: Pull and discard top of stack. BASIC will reset stack.

Line 460: Initialise indexing register.

Line 470: Get error number.

Line 480: Was it a 'Mistake' error?

Line 490: Branch to 'ignore' if not.

Line 500: Decrement BASIC text pointer offset.

Line 510: And then load it into the accumulator.

Line 520: Clear the carry flag.

Line 530: And add offset to low byte of text pointer.

Line 540: Save result.

Line 550: Branch to 'skip_1' if there is no carry.

Line 560: Else increment high bytes of text pointer.

Line 570: Entry to 'skip_1'.

Line 580: Get high byte of command table address.

Line 590: Store in high byte of secondary text pointer.

Line 600: Get low byte address of command table.

Line 610: Store in low byte of secondary text pointer.

Line 620: And again in text pointer offset.

Line 630: Entry point to the 'interpret' routine.

Line 640: Initialise indexing register for loop and to clear flags.

Line 650: Entry point to 'interpret_loop'.

Line 660: Increment indexing register.

Line 670: Get byte from the command table.

Line 680: If zero then command identified so branch to 'found_it'.

Line 690: Was it &FF and therefore the end of the command table?

Line 700: If it was then branch to 'ignore'.

Line 710: Is it the same as the corresponding byte in the program?

Line 720: If not branch to 'next_try'.

Line 730: Else branch to 'interpret_loop' to test next byte.

Line 740: Entry to 'found_it'.

Line 750: Save index in text pointer offset byte.

Line 760: Increment index.

Line 770: Get low byte execution address of command.

Line 780: And store in low byte of a vector.

Line 790: Increment index.

Line 800: Get high byte of execution address.

Line 810: And store in high byte of vector.

Line 820: Perform indirect jump, through vector to execution address of the identified command.

Line 830: Entry to 'next_try'.

Line 840: Increment index.

Line 850: Get byte from command table.

Line 860: Branch to 'next_try' if byte is not zero.

Lines 870 to 890: Move index past execution address.

Line 900: Clear the carry flag.

Line 910: Move index across into the accumulator.

Line 920: Add to low byte of command table address.

Line 930: And store back there.

Line 940: Branch to 'skip_2' if carry is clear.

Line 950: Else increment high byte.

Line 960: Entry to 'skip_2'.

Line 970: And jump back to 'interpret'.

Line 980: Entry to 'endcomm'.

Line 990: Check for end of statement.

Line 1000: And jump back into BASIC.

Line 1010: Command table marker.

Line 1020: Assemble ASCII string "PACK".

Line 1030: End of string marker.

Line 1040: Assemble execution address of PACK.

Line 1050: Assemble ASCII string "TEST".

Line 1060: End of string marker.

Line 1070: Assemble execution address of TEST.

Line 1080: Assemble ASCII string "BEEP".

Line 1090: End of string marker.

Line 1100: Assemble execution address of BEEP.

Line 1110: Assemble end of command table marker.

Lines 1120 to 2080: Machine code to execute PACK, TEST and BEEP.

Chapter Nine
Home Brew

The real fun in learning about how the ROM paging system works comes in writing your own home-brewed utilities ready to sit in an EPROM or sideways RAM so that they can be called by name from programs or directly at the keyboard. However, unless you can successfully market your firmware in 'best seller' proportions, it is unlikely that your program would be transferrable between Beebs. But, this is not a real problem if you are interested mainly in writing debugging aids, as these are designed to make your own programming life easier.

Write your own

In this chapter, several example programs are presented showing how the various service calls can be trapped and processed correctly to the desired result. In doing so a mini sideways ROM is developed, which I have christened 'BASIC tools'. This adds a further four commands to your micro's vocabulary, namely:

*BEEP   issues a beep on the speaker
*FNKEY   lists the function key definitions
*SCREEN   saves the current graphics screen to disc or tape
*VDU   lists the user-definable character definitions in decimal format.

Finally, at the end of the chapter, a simple hexadecimal and ASCII dump routine is implemented as a language to complete the set of sideways tutorial routines.

At this point I had better make an important point about assembling code into the sideways ROM area. I'm assuming first of all that you will be assembling the code into sideways RAM for testing purposes. In fact, this should be a standard procedure as it is very unlikely that any code you write will run first time. Blowing machine code directly into an EPROM before testing it will ultimately be both time-consuming and expensive. If sideways EPROM coding contains a bug, the EPROM must be erased and then reprogrammed before you can use it again. So, assuming that you are using sideways RAM, we had better distinguish between the two types. Basically, sideways RAM is available on boards specifically marketed as such and it is also available on many sideways ROM boards – a subject dealt with in the next chapter. If you are using the former then your code can normally be assembled directly from &8000 by setting the program counter variable, P%, directly, thus:

P%=&8000

Many sideways ROM boards which house sideways RAM allow this to take place but the assembly listing produced is incorrect – Fig. 9.1 shows what I mean. To check this, try assembling a short section of code to &8000 and look carefully at the assembly listing. This can be confusing so I prefer to

```
8000
8000
8000              OPT PASS
8000 C9           EQUB 0
8001 01 F0        EQUW 0
8003 1F 60 EA     JMP service_entry+diff%
8006 60           EQUB &82
8007 0E           EQUB offset MOD 256
8008 01           EQUB 1
8009              .title
8009 42 41 53
     49 43 00
     28 43 29
     31 39 38
     32 20 41
     63           EQUS "BASIC Tools 1.00"
8019 6F           EQUB 0
801A              .offset
801A 72           EQUB 0
801B 6E 0A 0D
     00 00 80
     00 00 A9
     84 20 F4
     FF           EQUS "(C) Love Byte"
8028 86           EQUB 0
8029              .service_entry
8029 06           PHA
802A 84 07        CMP #9
802C A9 83        BEQ help
802E 20           PLA
802F F4           RTS
8030              .help
8030 FF 84 18     JSR osnewl
8033 A2 00        LDX #&FF
8035              .helploop
```

```
8035 86          INX
8036 1F 8E 02 LDA title+diff%,X
8039 04 8E 03 JSR &FFE3
803C 04 CA    BNE helploop
803E 86 23 A2 JSR osnewl
8041 0A       PLA
8042 8E       RTS
```

Fig. 9.1. Code appearing to assemble incorrectly at &8000.

assemble the code elsewhere to generate a correct listing. All the listings here assume this assembly method, which works as follows. First, P% is set to &5000, so that the assembly listing is generated starting at &5000. To ensure that all absolute addresses are assembled correctly, an offset is included. This is done by defining a variable, 'diff%' in my listings, to the offset difference which is &3000 – obtained by performing &8000–&5000. All absolute addresses now have this difference added. I define this absolute address as being one that is &8000 or greater – in other words any JMP, JSR, LDA, etc. that accesses a location in the sideways ROM/RAM itself. The assembler just becomes

JSR print+diff%
JMP exit+diff%
LDA message+diff%,X

and so forth. The program examples should make this clearer.

After writing the program it must be assembled and loaded into sideways RAM. To do this, RUN the program and save the machine code generated, thus:

*SAVE MC 5000 5xxx

where 5xxx is the final value of P%+1.

Now the coding can be *LOADed in sideways RAM with

*LOAD MC 8000

Remember to add the 8000 to assemble the code in the correct location. Now all that remains to be done is to press BREAK to allow the MOS to reset and recognise that a new section of code is present in its paged ROM area!

There is one final advantage in assembling code in machine RAM in this way – it is immediately ready for blowing into EPROM directly from RAM and does not require any fancy coding to read each byte from sideways RAM.

Let us now progress to the sideways ROM/RAM programs. First, we'll deal with service ROM coding and to that end nine programs are presented here. In order, they are as follows:

(a) *HELP – responding to this command.
(b) *HELP BTOOL – responding to a specific *HELP.

(c) Command Table Test – implementing a command table and testing it.

(d) Command Table Finale – the complete command table and commands.

(e) Print Title String on BREAK – printing your ROM title on a reset.

(f) Claim Workspace – claiming private workspace.

(g) Auto-boot ROM – how to auto-boot your own ROM.

(h) OSBYTE – adding an extra OSBYTE call.

(i) OSWORD – adding an extra OSWORD call.

Rather than present all the above items in a single, twenty page long program I have broken each service call coding type down to form the basis of a single program. This restricts the program size to a manageable length and will allow you to see more readily just what is actually happening. This will result in a certain amount of repetition, particularly in the ROM header, but diligent use of the DELETE *SPOOL and *EXEC commands and COPY key will enable you to modify each program with the minimum of fuss.

The header

We have already seen that a sideways ROM is recognised by its header. Constructing your own header is straightforward and should present no real problems. A standard header is used throughout all the programs presented in this chapter; it is therefore worth saving this to tape or disc so that it can be reloaded quickly as required. A description of the header is presented with that of the first program below.

*HELP

Program 9.1 provides the BASIC and assembler text needed to process a *HELP service call, code 9. Contrary to what I said a moment or two ago it is well worth including a *HELP processing routine in software you are debugging, as by issuing the command it is immediately evident whether your sideways software is indeed present. If you know you have a working *HELP service routine and it will not respond then it is more likely that there isn't a bug in your software but in your hardware – or perhaps you forgot to load it into sideways RAM correctly. I've made that error on many an occasion!

```
10 REM Implement *HELP
20 REM (c) Bruce Smith October 1984
30 REM The BBC Micro ROM Book
40 :
50 osnewl=&FFE7
60 diff%=&3000
70 FOR PASS=0 TO 3 STEP 3
80 P%=&5000
```

```
 90 [
100 OPT PASS
110 EQUB 0
120 EQUW 0
130 JMP service_entry+diff%
140 EQUB &82
150 EQUB offset MOD 256
160 EQUB 1
170 .title
180 EQUS "BASIC Tools 1.00"
190 EQUB 0
200 .offset
210 EQUB 0
220 EQUS "(C) Love Byte"
230 EQUB 0
240 .service_entry
250 PHA
260 CMP #9
270 BEQ help
280 PLA
290 RTS
300 .help
310 JSR osnewl
320 LDX #&FF
330 .helploop
340 INX
350 LDA title+diff%,X
360 JSR &FFE3
370 BNE helploop
380 JSR osnewl
390 PLA
400 RTS
410 ]
420 NEXT
```

Program 9.1. Implementing *HELP.

Back to the listing. Two important variables to point out straight away are in lines 80 and 60. P% is set equal to &5000 in line 80 and the sideways ROM displacement is made good by the diff% variable set to &3000 in line 60.

Lines 110 to 240: These contain the header code. As mentioned, this is fairly standard in the following programs though the line numbers do vary from time to time. A brief description of the header is given here but will not be repeated in future listing commentary.

Lines 110 to 120: As there is no language entry point, set these three bytes to zero.

Line 130: Assemble JMP service entry address.

Line 140: Mark ROM type as service ROM only.

Line 150: Assemble copyright offset point by calculating low byte address.
Line 160: Version number 1.
Line 170: Mark title string with label.
Line 180: Assemble title string. This includes the ASCII version number in this instance to simplify coding.
Line 190: End of string marker.
Line 200: Copyright marker.
Line 220: Copyright string.
Line 230: End of string byte.
Line 240: Entry point for service entry.

*HELP requests are issued by the MOS with a service call 9. On entry to our routine at line 250, the service type is preserved by pushing it onto the hardware stack. The service type is compared with 9 and if they are alike a branch to 'help' is performed, else the stack is pulled and a simple RTS transfers control back to the MOS. The service call has now been identified and all that remains is to print out the ROM's title string. Marked by the label 'title' in line 170. Before doing this a new line is issued and the title printing loop (lines 330 to 370) entered, exiting only when the zero byte is encountered. Another new line is printed before balancing the stack and returning to the MOS.

Assemble and save the machine code as described above and then *LOAD back into position. Hit break to reset the system and then enter *HELP. All being well, the message

    BASIC tools 1.00

should have been issued among that by any other ROMs you may have present.

As the title string may contain ASCII characters, interesting effects can be created in title strings by embedding control codes here and there – for example, double height *HELP messages in MODE 7, if so desired!

*HELP BTOOL

The *HELP message can be extended to be ROM-specific by post-fixing it with a keyword that the ROM will recognise, upon which it will issue various details about the ROM – a list of its commands, for instance. Program 9.2 shows how this can be implemented. Basically, all we need to do after trapping the *HELP service call is to test the byte following it. If it is an ASCII return character, ASCII 13, then a simple *HELP is detected. If, on the other hand, this character is not an ASCII return, a specific *HELP request has been issued and each ROM must, in turn, test to see if it is relevant to its vocabulary.

```
10REM Implement *HELP BTOOL
20REM (c) Bruce Smith 1984
30REM The BBC Micro ROM Book
40REM :
50osnewl=&FFE7
60osasci=&FFE3
70diff%=&3000
80FOR PASS=0 TO 3 STEP 3
90P%=&5000
100[
110OPT PASS
120EQUB 0
130EQUW 0
140JMP service_entry+diff%
150EQUB &82
160EQUB offset MOD 256
170EQUB 1
180.title
190EQUS "BASIC Tools 1.00"
200EQUB 0
210.offset
220EQUB 0
230EQUS "(C) Love Byte"
240EQUB 0
250.service_entry
260PHA
270CMP #9
280BEQ help
290PLA
300RTS
310.help
320TYA
330PHA
340TXA
350PHA
360LDA (&F2),Y
370CMP #13
380BEQ over
390LDX #&FF
400DEY
410.btooloop
420INX
430INY
440LDA btool+diff%,X
450CMP (&F2),Y
460BEQ btooloop
470CMP #&FE
480BEQ details
490PLA
500TAX
```

```
510PLA
520TAY
530JMP return
540.over
550JSR printhelp+diff%
560PLA
570TAX
580PLA
590TAY
600.return
610PLA
620RTS
630.printhelp
640JSR osnewl
650LDX #&FF
660.helploop
670INX
680LDA title+diff%,X
690JSR osasci
700BNE helploop
710JSR osnewl
715PLA
720RTS
730:
740.details
750JSR printhelp+diff%
760LDX #&FF
770.detailoop
780INX
790LDA commands+diff%,X
800JSR osasci
810BNE detailoop
820JSR osnewl
830PLA
840TAX
850PLA
860TAY
870PLA
880RTS
890.commands
900EQUS"   BEEP"
910EQUB 13
920EQUS"   KEYS"
930EQUB 13
940EQUS"   SCREEN"
950EQUB 13
960EQUS"   VDU"
970EQUB 13
980EQUB 0
990.btool
```

```
1000EQUS "BTOOL"
1010EQUB &FE
1020J
1030NEXT
```

Program 9.2. Implementing *HELP BTOOL.

The header and *HELP test coding are the same as described for the previous listing. On entry to 'help' (line 310) both index registers are preserved on the stack as these will be destroyed and will need to be restored should our ROM not be identified as the relevant ROM. The vector at &F2, COMV, points to the H in the *HELP command while the Y register holds the post-indirect index to the first non-space character after the P. There is no need, therefore, to index the Y any further at this point. By loading the next non-space byte after the *HELP into the accumulator, ASCII 13 can be tested for (lines 360 to 380) and a branch to 'over' performed to process the simple *HELP as already described. The only difference is that the two index registers must be pulled to balance the stack along with the accumulator before returning to the MOS.

If the branch to 'over' is not performed then a specific *HELP has been detected. Our specific *HELP command is *HELP BTOOL, so the next step is to test for the ASCII string "BTOOL". This is performed in the 'btooloop' between lines 410 to 460, comparing the ASCII string in memory (indexing the Y register) with that in our loop up table – line 1000 (indexing the X register). This loop repeats until two unlike bytes are encountered. The accumulator is then tested for &FE, which is used to mark the end of the 'BTOOL' string (line 1010). If this is present, the command has been identified and the BEQ details (line 480) performed, otherwise the stack is pulled to restore the processor registers and control is passed back to the MOS.

The 'details' coding starts by printing the standard 'BASIC tools 1.00' message (line 750) followed by the command details held in the ASCII command table between lines 890 to 980. The printing loop is embedded in lines 770 to 810 and continues until a zero terminating byte is encountered, whereupon the stack is restored and control handed back to the MOS.

If you enter and save the program correctly, then on issuing the *HELP BTOOL command, the output on the screen should look a little like this:

*HELP BTOOL

BASIC tools 1.00
   BEEP
   FNKEY
   SCREEN
   VDU

Writing and testing the interpreter

To complete the sideways ROM/RAM service coding we must implement a simple interpreter to allow unrecognised commands to be identified and then executed. Program 9.3 lists the entire assembler for this. The basis of this listing is Program 9.2 as it handles both standard and specific *HELP calls, and the layout has been rearranged somewhat to accommodate the extra coding. Note also that the line numbers do not run concurrently – this is deliberate as this listing can then be readily extended to the final fully fledged version.

```
 10 REM BASIC Tools 1.25
 20 REM Test Command Interpreter
 30 REM (c) Bruce Smith 1984
 40 REM The BBC Micro ROM Book
 50 :
160 osnewl=&FFE7
170 osasci=&FFE3
180 comline=&F2
190 diff%=&3000
200 :
210 FOR PASS=0 TO 3 STEP 3
220 P%=&5000
230 [
240 OPT PASS
250 EQUB 0
260 EQUW 0
270 JMP service_entry+diff%
280 EQUB &82
290 EQUB offset MOD 256
300 EQUB 1
310 .title
320 EQUS "BASIC tools 1.25"
330 EQUB 0
340 .offset
350 EQUB 0
360 EQUS "(C) Love Byte"
370 EQUB 0
380 .service_entry
390 PHA
400 CMP #9
410 BEQ help
420 CMP #4
430 BEQ unrecognised
440 PLA
450 RTS
460 .help
470 TYA
480 PHA
```

```
490 TXA
500 PHA
510 LDA (comline),Y
520 CMP #13
530 BEQ over
540 LDX #&FF
550 DEY
560 .tableoop
570 INX
580 INY
590 LDA table+diff%,X
600 CMP (comline),Y
610 BEQ tableoop
620 CMP #&FE
630 BEQ details
640 PLA
650 TAX
660 PLA
670 TAY
680 JMP return+diff%
690 .over
700 JSR printhelp+diff%
710 PLA
720 TAX
730 PLA
740 TAY
750 .return
760 PLA
770 RTS
780 .printhelp
790 JSR osnewl
800 LDX #&FF
810 .helploop
820 INX
830 LDA title+diff%,X
840 JSR osasci
850 BNE helploop
860 JSR osnewl
870 RTS
880 :
890 .details
900 JSR printhelp+diff%
910 LDX #&FF
920 .detailoop
930 INX
940 LDA commands+diff%,X
950 JSR osasci
960 BNE detailoop
970 JSR osnewl
980 PLA
```

```
 990 TAX
1000 PLA
1010 TAY
1020 PLA
1030 RTS
1040 .unrecognised
1050 TYA
1060 PHA
1070 TXA
1080 PHA
1090 LDX #&FF
1100 DEY
1110 STY &100
1120 .ctloop
1130 INX
1140 INY
1150 LDA table+diff%,X
1160 BMI found
1170 CMP (comline),Y
1180 BEQ ctloop
1190 .again
1200 INX
1210 LDA table+diff%,X
1220 BPL again
1230 CMP #&FF
1240 BEQ out
1250 INX
1260 LDY &100
1270 JMP ctloop+diff%
1280 :
1290 .out
1300 .nothisrom
1310 PLA
1320 TAX
1330 PLA
1340 TAY
1350 PLA
1360 RTS
1370 .found
1380 CMP #&FF
1390 BEQ nothisrom
1400 STA &39
1410 INX
1420 LDA table+diff%,X
1430 STA &38
1440 JMP (&38)
1450 :
1460 \ set up Command Table
1470 .table
1480 EQUS "BEEP"
```

```
1490 EQUB (beep+diff%) DIV 256
1500 EQUB (beep+diff%) MOD 256
1510 EQUS "SCREEN"
1520 EQUB (beep+diff%) DIV 256
1530 EQUB (beep+diff%) MOD 256
1540 EQUS "FNKEY"
1550 EQUB (beep+diff%) DIV 256
1560 EQUB (beep+diff%) MOD 256
1570 EQUS "VDU"
1580 EQUB (beep+diff%) DIV 256
1590 EQUB (beep+diff%) MOD 256
1600 EQUB &FF
1610 :
1620 .commands
1630 EQUS"    BEEP"
1640 EQUB 13
1650 EQUS"    FNKEY"
1660 EQUB 13
1670 EQUS"    SCREEN"
1680 EQUB 13
1690 EQUS"    VDU"
1700 EQUB 13
1710 EQUB 0
1720 :
1730 \ *BEEP
1740 .beep
1750 LDA #7
1760 JSR &FFE3
1770 PLA
1780 PLA
1790 PLA
1800 LDA #0
1810 RTS
1820 ] NEXT
```

Program 9.3. Testing the Command Table.

Looking at line 420 of the listing we can see that an extra service call is being tested for. This is service call 4, issued by the MOS to inform sideways ROMs that an unrecognised command has been issued. To see if this unrecognised command is one present in our ROM we must first trap this call and then proceed to compare the unrecognised command with each of those in our command table. If a match if found, the command's execution address can be extracted and jumped to. For the purpose of explanation, we are interested in the assembler held between lines 1040 to 1600.

Let us first examine the construction of the command table, lines 1480 to 1600. It consists of the ASCII command string, followed by the command's two-byte execution address stored high byte first. This is followed by the next command string and so forth until the last command execution address

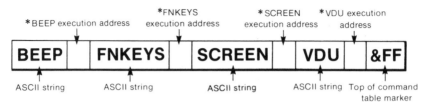

Fig. 9.2. The BASIC Tools Command Table.

is terminated by &FF. Figure 9.2 shows all this diagramatically. There are two things to point out at this stage. First, as you may have noticed, the execution address assembled for each command is, in fact, that of *BEEP. This is quite deliberate as the code to execute this, equivalent to VDU 7, is hardly likely to contain any bugs so that we can first concentrate on getting the interpreter right. If, on executing each command, a beep occurs correctly, we can then move on to adding and debugging the coding for each command in term.

The second point concerns the manner in which the execution addresses are stored – high byte first, which is not normal 6502 convention. This is because we are then assured of a negative byte to mark the end of the ASCII command string which can be used as a control parameter in the comparison loop. The byte will be negative as all execution addresses have got to be between &8000 to &BFFF for them to be within the sideways ROM area!

The COMV at &F2 and index in the Y register point to the first character in the unrecognised command. Using the X register as an absolute index into the command table, each byte can be compared in turn. Because the Y register's indexing contents are of paramount importance a copy of its original value minus one must be on hand – in this instance, a copy is written on the first byte of the stack at &100 (line 1110).

The identification loop begins by incrementing both registers and then loading a byte from the command table. If this byte is negative then the command may have been identified and a branch to 'found' is performed. If the byte is positive then it is compared with the corresponding byte in the unrecognised string (lines 1150 to 1170). If they are the same, the loop is reiterated via a branch to 'ctloop' (line 1180). If the bytes are unlike then the next command in the command table must be sought by indexing the X register through it until the negative byte is encountered (lines 1190 to 1220). Moving past the address bytes, the third byte is tested for &FF to see if the end of the command table has been reached. If so, a branch to 'out' takes place, otherwise the index registers are reset and the 'ctloop' re-entered (line 1270).

The 'out' and 'nothisrom' routines are entered at lines 1290 and 1300 where the processor registers are restored prior to a return to the MOS. Assuming that the command is identified, the 'found' routine at 1370 is entered where the command's two-byte execution address is extracted from the table and placed in a zero page vector prior to an indirect jump taking place (lines 1380 to 1440). Note that it is the responsibility of the identified command's coding to ensure that the ROM is exited with the stack correctly pulled. As the command has been processed there is no need to ensure that each processor register is restored correctly, just that the accumulator returns with zero (lines 1770 to 1810).

Testing the interpreter is simple. First enter, RUN, save and reload the machine code as described earlier. After hitting BREAK, test the *HELP commands to ensure that the software is correctly installed. Now enter each new command in turn:

```
*BEEP
*FNKEY
*SCREEN
*VDU
```

A beep on the internal speaker should be issued after each command. If not or the Beeb hangs up, re-check your assembler for bugs.

The Complete Interpreter

Once the interpreter is known to be functioning correctly we can move on to the next step of adding the coding for the other three commands. This is best done command by command, testing each as you go. This makes it easier from the debugging point of view as you always know just where in the program the bug has been introduced.

As a matter of habit it is also a good idea to write your utility routines in two stages. The first stage is to write it in BASIC! This assures you that the thing will work and also allows you to identify the various stages that will be required in converting your idea to assembler. It also has the added advantage of allowing you to see what the final output will look like. The second stage is to convert the BASIC into assembler and get it fully debugged before you transfer it into sideways RAM.

The three routines provided here are pinched from my other book, *The BBC Micro Machine Code Portfolio* also published by Granada-Collins, so I have three fully tested and debugged routines to hand.

The listing for the complete interpreter is provided in Program 9.4, but do not simply sit down and type this in one go; instead, proceed as described on page 122 for the minimum of heartache.

```
10 REM BASIC Tools 1.25
20 REM *BEEP, *FNKEY, *SCREEN, *VDU
30 REM (c) Bruce Smith 1984
40 REM The BBC Micro ROM Book
50 :
60 ssaved=&56
```

```
 70 paramblk=&60
 80 soft_base=&50
 90 vdu_character=&52
100 addition_bytes=&53
110 flag=&55
120 key=&45
130 keystart=&46
140 endpointer=&47
150 offset1=&48
160 osnewl=&FFE7
170 osasci=&FFE3
180 comline=&F2
190 diff%=&3000
200 :
210 FOR PASS=0 TO 3 STEP 3
220 P%=&5000
230 [
240 OPT PASS
250 EQUB 0
260 EQUW 0
270 JMP service_entry+diff%
280 EQUB &82
290 EQUB offset MOD 256
300 EQUB 1
310 .title
320 EQUS "BASIC tools 1.25"
330 EQUB 0
340 .offset
350 EQUB 0
360 EQUS "(C) Love Byte"
370 EQUB 0
380 .service_entry
390 PHA
400 CMP #9
410 BEQ help
420 CMP #4
430 BEQ unrecognised
440 PLA
450 RTS
460 .help
470 TYA
480 PHA
490 TXA
500 PHA
510 LDA (comline),Y
520 CMP #13
530 BEQ over
540 LDX #&FF
550 DEY
560 .tableoop
```

```
 570 INX
 580 INY
 590 LDA table+diff%,X
 600 CMP (comline),Y
 610 BEQ tableoop
 620 CMP #&FE
 630 BEQ details
 640 PLA
 650 TAX
 660 PLA
 670 TAY
 680 JMP return+diff%
 690 .over
 700 JSR printhelp+diff%
 710 PLA
 720 TAX
 730 PLA
 740 TAY
 750 .return
 760 PLA
 770 RTS
 780 .printhelp
 790 JSR osnewl
 800 LDX #&FF
 810 .helploop
 820 INX
 830 LDA title+diff%,X
 840 JSR osasci
 850 BNE helploop
 860 JSR osnewl
 870 RTS
 880 :
 890 .details
 900 JSR printhelp+diff%
 910 LDX #&FF
 920 .detailoop
 930 INX
 940 LDA commands+diff%,X
 950 JSR osasci
 960 BNE detailoop
 970 JSR osnewl
 980 PLA
 990 TAX
1000 PLA
1010 TAY
1020 PLA
1030 RTS
1040 .unrecognised
1050 TYA
1060 PHA
```

```
1070 TXA
1080 PHA
1090 LDX #&FF
1100 DEY
1110 STY &100
1120 .ctloop
1130 INX
1140 INY
1150 LDA table+diff%,X
1160 BMI found
1170 CMP (comline),Y
1180 BEQ ctloop
1190 .again
1200 INX
1210 LDA table+diff%,X
1220 BPL again
1230 CMP #&FF
1240 BEQ out
1250 INX
1260 LDY &100
1270 JMP ctloop+diff%
1280 :
1290 .out
1300 .nothisrom
1310 PLA
1320 TAX
1330 PLA
1340 TAY
1350 PLA
1360 RTS
1370 .found
1380 CMP #&FF
1390 BEQ nothisrom
1400 STA &39
1410 INX
1420 LDA table+diff%,X
1430 STA &38
1440 JMP (&38)
1450 :
1460 \ set up Command Table
1470 .table
1480 EQUS "BEEP"
1490 EQUB (beep+diff%) DIV 256
1500 EQUB (beep+diff%) MOD 256
1510 EQUS "SCREEN"
1520 EQUB (screen+diff%) DIV 256
1530 EQUB (screen+diff%) MOD 256
1540 EQUS "FNKEY"
1550 EQUB (keys+diff%) DIV 256
1560 EQUB (keys+diff%) MOD 256
```

```
1570 EQUS "VDU"
1580 EQUB (vdu+diff%) DIV 256
1590 EQUB (vdu+diff%) MOD 256
1600 EQUB &FF
1610 :
1620 .commands
1630 EQUS"    BEEP"
1640 EQUB 13
1650 EQUS"    FNKEY"
1660 EQUB 13
1670  EQUS"    SCREEN"
1680 EQUB 13
1690 EQUS"    VDU"
1700 EQUB 13
1710 EQUB 0
1720 :
1730 \ *BEEP
1740 .beep
1750 LDA #7
1760 JSR &FFE3
1770 PLA
1780 PLA
1790 PLA
1800 LDA #0
1810 RTS
1820 :
1830 \ *FNKEY
1840 .keys
1850 LDA #0
1860 STA key
1870 STA offset1
1880 .mainloop
1890 JSR &FFE7
1900 JSR printwordkey+diff%
1910 LDX key
1920 LDA numbertable+diff%,X
1930 INX
1940 JSR &FFEE
1950 LDA numbertable+diff%,X
1960 JSR &FFEE
1970 INX
1980 STX key
1990 LDA #32
2000 JSR &FFEE
2010 LDX offset1
2020 LDA &B00,X
2030 STA keystart
2040 INC keystart
2050 LDA &B10
2060 STA endpointer
```

```
2070 LDX #&F
2080 .keyend
2090 LDA &B00,X
2100 CMP endpointer
2110 BCS nexttry
2120 CMP keystart
2130 BCC nexttry
2140 STA endpointer
2150 .nexttry
2160 DEX
2170 BPL keyend
2180 LDA endpointer
2190 CMP keystart
2200 BCC nextkey
2210 LDX keystart
2220 .printdef
2230 LDA &B00,X
2240 CMP #128
2250 BCC asciichr
2260 PHA
2270 LDA #ASC"|"
2280 JSR &FFEE
2290 LDA #ASC"!"
2300 JSR &FFEE
2310 PLA
2320 AND #&7F
2330 .asciichr
2340 CMP #32
2350 BCS notcontrol
2360 PHA
2370 LDA #ASC"|"
2380 JSR &FFEE
2390 PLA
2400 CLC
2410 ADC #64
2420 JSR &FFEE
2430 JMP nextcharacter+diff%
2440 .notcontrol
2450 CMP #127
2460 BNE over1
2470 LDA #ASC"|"
2480 JSR &FFEE
2490 LDA #ASC"?"
2500 JSR &FFEE
2510 JMP nextcharacter+diff%
2520 .over1
2530 CMP#124
2540 BNE not
2550 LDA #ASC"|"
2560 JSR &FFEE
```

```
2570 JSR &FFEE
2580 JMP nextcharacter+diff%
2590 .not
2600 JSR &FFEE
2610 .nextcharacter
2620 CPX endpointer
2630 BEQ nextkey
2640 INX
2650 JMP printdef+diff%
2660 .nextkey
2670 INC offset1
2680 LDA offset1
2690 CMP #16
2700 BNE notfinished
2710 JSR &FFE7
2720 PLA
2730 PLA
2740 PLA
2750 LDA #0
2760 RTS
2770 :
2780 .notfinished
2790 JMP mainloop+diff%
2800 .printwordkey
2810 LDY #6
2820 .nextletter
2830 LDA spellkey+diff%,Y
2840 JSR &FFEE
2850 DEY
2860 BNE nextletter
2870 RTS
2880 :
2890 .numbertable
2900 EQUS" 0 1 2 3 4 5 6 7 "
2910 EQUS"8 9101112131415"
2920 .spellkey
2930 EQUS"  YEK* "
2940 :
2950 \ *VDU
2960 .vdu
2970 JSR set_up_screen+diff%
2980 LDA #224
2990 STA vdu_character
3000 LDA #&C
3010 STA soft_base+1
3020 LDA #0
3030 STA soft_base
3040 STA addition_bytes
3050 STA addition_bytes+1
3060 TAY
```

```
3070 .main_loop
3080 JSR test_for_definition+diff%
3090 LDA addition_bytes
3100 BNE print_definition
3110 LDA addition_bytes+1
3120 BNE print_definition
3130 JSR update+diff%
3140 BNE main_loop
3150 JMP exit+diff%
3160 .print_definition
3170 LDA vdu_character
3180 JSR binary_decimal_print+diff%
3190 LDA #ASC":"
3200 JSR &FFEE
3210 LDA #ASC" "
3220 JSR &FFEE
3230 LDY #0
3240 .loop
3250 LDA (soft_base),Y
3260 JSR binary_decimal_print+diff%
3270 LDA #ASC","
3280 JSR &FFEE
3290 INY
3300 CPY #8
3310 BNE loop
3320 JSR update+diff%
3330 LDA#0
3340 STA addition_bytes
3350 STA addition_bytes+1
3360 TAY
3370 LDA #13
3380 JSR &FFE3
3390 JMP main_loop+diff%
3400 .binary_decimal_print
3410 LDX #0
3420 STX flag
3430 .hundreds
3440 CMP#100
3450 BCC no_hundreds
3460 SBC #100
3470 INX
3480 STX flag
3490 JMP hundreds+diff%
3500 .no_hundreds
3510 JSR print_decimal+diff%
3520 LDX #0
3530 .tens
3540 CMP #10
3550 BCC no_tens
3560 SBC #10
```

```
3570 INX
3580 JMP tens+diff%
3590 .no_tens
3600 JSR print_decimal+diff%
3610 CLC
3620 ADC #ASC"0"
3630 JMP &FFEE
3640 .print_decimal
3650 PHA
3660 TXA
3670 ADC #ASC"0"
3680 CMP #ASC"0"
3690 BNE no_zero
3700 LDX flag
3710 BNE no_zero
3720 LDA #32
3730 .no_zero
3740 JSR &FFEE
3750 PLA
3760 RTS
3770 .test_for_definition
3780 LDY#7
3790 .check_loop
3800 LDA (soft_base),Y
3810 CLC
3820 ADC addition_bytes
3830 STA addition_bytes
3840 BCC no_carry
3850 INC addition_bytes+1
3860 .no_carry
3870 DEY
3880 BPL check_loop
3890 RTS
3900 .set_up_screen
3910 LDX#0
3920 .next_character
3930 LDA vdutitle+diff%,X
3940 BMI done
3950 JSR &FFEE
3960 INX
3970 JMP next_character+diff%
3980 .done
3990 RTS
4000 .vdutitle
4010 EQUB 22
4020 EQUB 6
4030 EQUD &0D0A0D0A
4040 EQUS"*** SOFT CHR"
4050 EQUS" CHARACTER "
4060 EQUS"DEFINITIONS ***"
```

```
4070 EQUD &0D0A0D0A
4080 EQUB 255
4090 .update
4100 CLC
4110 LDA soft_base
4120 ADC#8
4130 STA soft_base
4140 INC vdu_character
4150 BEQ exit
4160 RTS
4170 .exit
4180 JSR &FFE7
4190 PLA
4200 PLA
4210 PLA
4220 PLA
4230 PLA
4240 LDA #0
4250 RTS
4260 :
4270 \ #SCREEN
4280 .screen
4290 LDX #18
4300 .copy
4310 LDA constants+diff%,X
4320 STA paramblk,X
4330 DEX
4340 BPL copy
4350 LDX #7
4360 .string
4370 LDA filename+diff%,X
4380 STA ssaved,X
4390 DEX
4400 BPL string
4410 LDA #135
4420 JSR &FFF4
4430 TYA
4440 BEQ dump1
4450 CMP#3
4460 BCC dump1
4470 CMP#4
4480 BEQ dump2
4490 CMP#5
4500 BEQ dump2
4510 CMP #7
4520 BEQ teletext
4530 .error
4540 LDY #0
4550 .messageloop
4560   LDA message+diff%,Y
4570 BEQ finished
4580 JSR &FFE3
```

```
4590 INY
4600 BNE messageloop
4610 .finished
4620 PLA
4630 PLA
4640 PLA
4650 RTS
4660 :
4670 .dump1
4680 LDA #&30
4690 STA paramblk+3
4700 STA paramblk+7
4710 STA paramblk+&0B
4720 LDA #0
4730 JMP osfile+diff%
4740 .dump2
4750 LDA #&58
4760 STA paramblk+3
4770 STA paramblk+7
4780 STA paramblk+&0B
4790 LDA#0
4800 JMP osfile+diff%
4810 .teletext
4820 LDA #&7C
4830 STA paramblk+3
4840 STA paramblk+7
4850 STA paramblk+&0B
4860 LDA #0
4870 .osfile
4880 LDX #paramblk MOD 256
4890 LDY #paramblk DIV 256
4900 JMP &FFDD
4910 .filename
4920 EQUS"SSAVED"
4930 EQUB 13
4940 .constants
4950 EQUB ssaved MOD 256
4960 EQUB ssaved DIV 256
4970 EQUD&3000
4980 EQUD 0
4990 EQUD&3000
5000 EQUD&7FFF
5010 .message
5020 EQUB 7
5030 EQUS"Not a graphics Mode"
5040 EQUB 13
5050 EQUB 0
5060 ]
5070 NEXT
```

Program 9.4. The Complete BASIC Tools Sideways ROM.

Using Program 9.3 as your working base, add lines 60 to 150 from Program 9.4 to complete the variable assignments. Now we can add the *FNKEY coding. Delete line 1820 and now add lines 1820 to 2930 from Program 9.4 plus the following end line,

> 2940] NEXT

Now edit the command table lines 1550 and 1560 to point to the 'keys' label thus,

> 1550 EQUB (keys+diff%) DIV 256
> 1560 EQUB (keys+diff%) MOD 256

RUN the program and correct any errors, reassemble, save the machine code and reload it into sideways RAM. Try *HELP, *BEEP and, if all is well, *FNKEY. If everything is okay, a list of function keys should have appeared down the left-hand side of the screen. Try entering a few *KEY definitions and re-executing *FNKEY to ensure that these are printed correctly. Figure 9.3 shows a typical listing produced by the command.

```
*KEY   0 CALL &AOO!M
*KEY   1 CLS!M
*KEY   2 *GREPL!M
*KEY   3 LIST!M
*KEY   4 *ASSFORM!M
*KEY   5 *INSPECT
*KEY   6 *BASFORM!M
*KEY   7 FORN=&70 TO &7F:P.?N:N.!M
*KEY   8 *EXMON!M
*KEY   9 *BASIC!M
*KEY  10 OLD!MLIST!M
*KEY  11
*KEY  12
*KEY  13
*KEY  14
*KEY  15
```

Fig. 9.3. Typical output of *FNKEY.

The interpreter can now be extended to incorporate the *VDU command. To do this, delete line 2940 and enter lines 2940 to 4250 from Program 9.4, adding a final line:

> 4260] NEXT

Lines 1580 and 1590 need to be edited to assemble the correct execution address in the command table thus

> 1580 EQUB (vdu+diff%) DIV 256
> 1590 EQUB (vdu+diff%) MOD 256

Repeating the process, test each command in turn, culminating with *VDU, whereupon the screen should go into MODE 6 and a list of user-definable character definitions be printed out. Originally, only a few may be displayed as none will probably be present other than the odd bit of garbage in the character buffer. So, to ensure that everything is hunky dory, enter a VDU 23 definition yourself. For example, try

VDU 23,234,88,77,66,55,44,33,22,11

That's pretty distinctive. Now re-enter the command *VDU and see if this has been printed correctly. If it has not, then you need to do a bit of debugging! Figure 9.4 shows a typical *VDU output.

The last step is to add the *SCREEN coding by entering lines 4260 to 5070 and altering lines 1520 and 1630 in the command table.

1520 EQUB (screen+diff%) DIV 256
1530 EQUB (screen+diff%) MOD 256

Once again, go through the motions and after loading the assembled machine code into sideways RAM, test each command, saving *SCREEN

```
*** SOFT CHR CHARACTER DEFINITIONS ***

224:   32,165, 12,169,224,133,114,169,
225:   12,133,113,169,  0,133,112,133,
226: 115,133,116,168, 32,148, 12,165,
227: 115,208, 12,165,116,208,  8, 32,
228: 227, 12,208,240, 76,239, 12,165,
229: 114, 32, 89, 12,169, 58, 32,238,
230: 255,169, 32, 32,238,255,160,  0,
231: 177,112, 32, 89, 12,169, 44, 32,
232: 238,255,200,192,  8,208,241, 32,
233: 227, 12,169,  0,133,115,133,116,
234: 168,169, 13, 32,227,255, 76, 20,
235:  12,162,  0,134,117,201,100,144,
236:   8,233,100,232,134,117, 76, 93,
237:  12, 32,129, 12,162,  0,201, 10,
238: 144,  6,233, 10,232, 76,110, 12,
239:  32,129, 12, 24,105, 48, 76,238,
240: 255, 72,138,105, 48,201, 48,208,
241:   6,166,117,208,  2,169, 32, 32,
242: 238,255,104, 96,160,  7,177,112,
243:  24,101,115,133,115,144,  2,230,
244: 116,136, 16,242, 96,162,  0,189,
245: 180, 12, 48,  7, 32,238,255,232,
246:  76,167, 12, 96, 10, 13, 10, 13,
247:  42, 42, 42, 32, 83, 79, 70, 84,
248:  32, 67, 72, 82, 32, 67, 72, 65,
249:  82, 65, 67, 84, 69, 82, 32, 68,
250:  69, 70, 73, 78, 73, 84, 73, 79,
251:  78, 83, 32, 42, 42, 42, 10, 13,
252:  10, 13,255, 24,165,112,105,  8,
253: 133,112,230,114,240,  1, 96, 32,
254: 231,255,104,104, 96,  0,  0,  0,
```

Fig. 9.4. Typical output of *VDU.

till last. Now in MODE 7 enter *SCREEN, making sure you have a blank, formatted disc in your drive, and all being well the screen memory should be saved under the filename SSAVED. Cataloguing your disc should reveal this. To ensure that it has been saved correctly, simply load the screen memory back in:

*LOAD SSCREEN

Don't worry if the screen looks out of sync; this is quite probable especially if you have scrolled it since issuing the *SCREEN command, due to the way the teletext chip maps the screen memory. Repeat the process in other MODEs. In non-graphics modes, the error message 'Not a graphics MODE' should be generated.

Hopefully, now you have a fully fledged working sideways RAM. Let us look now at a few ways of adding extras to the interpreter.

Look, I'm here

To inform the programmer that a particular ROM is present in the Beeb, its title string can be printed onto the screen whenever the micro is powered up or BREAK is pressed. The DFS does this, for example, as should the current language. There are several ways in which this can be performed, but the simplest is to trap the first service call issued by the MOS, service call 1, and use it to instigate the printing of the title string. Program 9.5 shows the way.

```
 10 REM Print title string on BREAK
 20 REM (c) Bruce Smith 1984
 30 REM The BBC Micro ROM Book
 40 REM :
 50 osnewl =&FFE7
 60 osasci =&FFE3
 70 diff%=&3000
 80 FOR PASS=0 TO 3 STEP 3
 90 P%=&5000
100 [
110 OPT PASS
120 EQUB 0
130 EQUW 0
140 JMP service_entry+diff%
150 EQUB &82
160 EQUB offset MOD 256
170 EQUB 1
180 .title
190 EQUS "BASIC Tools 1.00"
200 EQUB 0
210 .offset
```

```
220 EQUB 0
230 EQUS "(C) Love Byte"
240 EQUB 0
250 .service_entry
260 PHA
270 CMP #1
280 BEQ handle
290 PLA
300 RTS
310 .handle
320 TYA
330 PHA
340 TXA
350 PHA
360 JSR osnewl
370 LDX #&FF
380 .printloop
390 INX
400 LDA title+diff%,X
410 JSR osasci
420 BNE printloop
430 JSR osnewl
440 PLA
450 TAX
460 PLA
470 TAY
480 PLA
490 LDA #0
500 RTS
510 ]
520 NEXT
```

Program 9.5. Print title string on BREAK.

The listing should be self-explanatory. If service call 1 is detected (line 270), a branch to 'handle' is performed (line 280). Once here, the ASCII title string in the ROM header is printed to the screen (lines 360 to 430) before a return to the MOS.

On setting up the code in sideways RAM and pressing BREAK, the screen should look a bit like this:

BASIC tools 1.00
BBC Computer 32K
Acorn DFS
BASIC

though the actual format may vary depending on what ROMs you have present.

Claim yer stake

As your sideways ROM software grows in complexity the need may well arise for you to store your own ROM data so that it is free from possible corruption by other sideways ROM firmware. This can be achieved by claiming private ROM workspace by trapping and processing service call 2, which is issued by the MOS on a hard or soft break. Program 9.6 shows how.

When service call 2 is issued, the Y register holds the current value assigned to PAGE. Your ROM coding must increment this accordingly for

```
 10 REM Claim 1 page private workspace
 20 REM (c) Bruce Smith 1984
 30 REM The BBC Micro ROM Book
 40 REM :
 50 diff%=&3000
 60 FOR PASS=0 TO 3 STEP 3
 70 P%=&5000
 80 [
 90 OPT PASS
100 EQUB 0
110 EQUW 0
120 JMP service_entry+diff%
130 EQUB &82
140 EQUB offset MOD 256
150 EQUB 1
160 .title
170 EQUS "BASIC Tools 1.00"
180 EQUB 0
190 .offset
200 EQUB 0
210 EQUS "(C) Love Byte"
220 EQUB 0
230 .service_entry
240 PHA
250 CMP #2
260 BEQ check
270 PLA
280 RTS
290 .check
300 TYA
310 STA &DF0,X
320 INY
330 PLA
340 LDA #0
350 RTS
360 ]
370 NEXT
```

Program 9.6. Claim one page private workspace.

each page of memory required. However, before doing so, it must store the Y register's value, and therefore the start page of your ROM's private workspace in the private workspace byte assigned to your ROM. On return from the call, the Y register contains the new PAGE value. Line by line, the private workspace claim code between lines 240 to 350 reads like this:

Line 240: Save accumulator on stack.
Line 250: Is it private workspace claim?
Line 260: Branch to 'check' if it is.
Line 270: Else pull stack,
Line 280: and return to MOS.
Line 290: Entry to private workspace claim.
Line 300: Move current PAGE value into accumulator,
Line 310: and save in base byte using ROM number in X register as an index to correct byte offset.
Line 320: Increment Y once to claim one page of private workspace.
Line 330: Pull stack to balance entry push.
Line 340: Clear accumulator to signal service call processed.
Line 350: Return back to MOS.

A boot up the Eighties!

As we saw in the description of ROM service calls in Chapter 3, ROMs may be auto-booted to perform a specific task on BREAK. For example, the Acorn DFS may be selected as the filing system, if it is not already the priority system, by executing D-BREAK – that is, by holding the D key down and then hitting the BREAK key. The routine provided in Program 9.7 shows how the combination C-BREAK can be used to catalogue a disc automatically.

```
 10 REM CAT disc on C-BREAK
 20 REM (c) Bruce Smith 1984
 30 REM The BBC Micro ROM Book
 40 REM :
 50 diff%=&3000
 60 FOR PASS=0 TO 3 STEP 3
 70 P%=&5000
 80 [
 90 OPT PASS
100 EQUB 0
110 EQUW 0
120 JMP service_entry+diff%
130 EQUB &82
140 EQUB offset MOD 256
150 EQUB 1
160 .title
170 EQUS "BASIC Tools 1.00"
```

```
180 EQUB 0
190 .offset
200 EQUB 0
210 EQUS "(C) Love Byte"
220 EQUB 0
230 .service_entry
240 PHA
250 CMP #3
260 BEQ handle
270 PLA
280 RTS
290 .handle
300 TYA
310 PHA
320 TXA
330 PHA
340 LDA #&7A
350 JSR &FFF4
360 CPX #&52
370 BNE out
380 LDA #&F
390 JSR &FFF4
400 LDA #&8A
410 LDX #0
420 LDY #ASC"*"
430 JSR &FFF4
440 LDY #ASC"D"
450 JSR &FFF4
460 LDY #ASC"."
470 JSR &FFF4
480 LDY #13
490 JSR &FFF4
500 LDA #&8A
510 LDX #0
520 LDY #ASC"*"
530 JSR &FFF4
540 LDY #ASC"."
550 JSR &FFF4
560 LDY #13
570 JSR &FFF4
580 .out
590 PLA
600 TAX
610 PLA
620 TAY
630 PLA
640 LDA #0
650 RTS
660 ]
670 NEXT
```

Program 9.7. Auto-booting a ROM to *CAT a disc.

Hex	Dec.	Key	Hex	Dec.	Key
&00	0	SHIFT	&40	64	CAPS LOCK
&01	1	CTRL	&41	65	A
&02	2	bit 7	&42	66	X
&03	3	bit 6	&43	67	F
&04	4	bit 5	&44	68	Y
&05	5	bit 4	&45	69	J
&06	6	bit 3	&46	70	K
&07	7	bit 2	&47	71	@
&08	8	bit 1	&48	72	:
&09	9	bit 0	&49	73	RETURN
&10	16	Q	&50	80	SHIFT LOCK
&11	17	3	&51	81	S
&12	18	4	&52	82	C
&13	19	5	&53	83	G
&14	20	f4	&54	84	H
&15	21	8	&55	85	N
&16	22	f7	&56	86	L
&17	23	-	&57	87	;
&18	24	^	&58	88	]
&19	25	LEFT CURSOR	&59	89	DELETE
&20	32	f0	&60	96	TAB
&21	33	W	&61	97	Z
&22	34	E	&62	98	SPACE
&23	35	T	&63	99	V
&24	36	7	&64	100	B
&25	37	9	&65	101	M
&26	38	I	&66	102	,
&27	39	0	&67	103	.
&28	40	_	&68	104	/
&29	41	DOWN CURSOR	&69	105	COPY
&30	48	1	&70	112	ESCAPE
&31	49	2	&71	113	f1
&32	50	D	&72	114	f2
&33	51	R	&73	115	f3
&34	52	6	&74	116	f5
&35	53	U	&75	117	f6
&36	54	O	&76	118	f8
&37	55	P	&77	119	f9
&38	56	[	&78	120	\
&39	57	UP CURSOR	&79	121	RIGHT CURSOR

Fig. 9.5. Internal key numbers.

The service call that needs to be trapped is service call 3 and this is performed in lines 240 and 250, passing control to 'handle' commencing at line 290. Once here, the index registers are preserved on the hardware stack (lines 300 to 330). The next step is to 'look' at the keyboard to detect any other key press. This is performed by calling OSBYTE &7A (lines 340 and 350), which will return the *internal* key number of any key detected, a list of which is provided in Fig. 9.5, in the X register.

The internal key code for the letter C is &52 and this is detected by line 360. If it is found then the OSBYTE &8A buffer insert is called appropriately to select first the disc filing system and then perform a catalogue by inserting the DFS commands

  *D.
  *.

into the input buffer respectively (lines 400 to 570). After this, the stack is restored, the accumulator cleared and a return to the MOS performed.

OSWORD squares

Service call 8 allows the programmer to implement his or her own OSWORD calls by using an unassigned OSWORD code number. On entry to the routine the bytes at &EF, &F0 and &F1 contain the accumulator, X and Y register values, respectively. As with other OSWORD calls, the index register must be used to pass the address of a parameter block where the routine expects to find its information.

Program 9.8 provides OSWORD call &A0 which will plot a four-sided

```
 10 REM Implement new OSWORD call &A0
 20 REM (C) Bruce Smith October 1984
 30 REM The BBC Micro ROM Book
 40 :
 50 oswrch=&FFEE
 60 count=&45
 70 param=&F0
 80 diff%=&3000
 90 FOR PASS=0 TO 3 STEP 3
100 P%=&5000
110 [
120 OPT PASS
130 EQUB 0
140 EQUW 0
150 JMP service_entry+diff%
160 EQUB &82
170 EQUB offset MOD 256
180 EQUB 1
190 .title
```

```
200 EQUS "BASIC Tools 1.00"
210 EQUB 0
220 .offset
230 EQUB 0
240 EQUS "(C) Love Byte"
250 EQUB 0
260 .service_entry
270 PHA
280 CMP #8
290 BEQ osword
300 PLA
310 RTS
320 :
330 .osword
340 LDA &EF
350 CMP #&A0
360 BEQ yes
370 PLA
380 RTS
390 .yes
400 LDA #3
410 STA count
420 LDY #0
430 LDA #25
440 JSR oswrch
450 LDA #4
460 JSR oswrch
470 LDX #4
480 .move
490 LDA (param),Y
500 JSR oswrch
510 INY
520 DEX
530 BNE move
540 .redo
550 LDA #25
560 JSR oswrch
570 LDA #6
580 JSR oswrch
590 LDX #4
600 .draw2
610 LDA (param),Y
620 JSR oswrch
630 INY
640 DEX
650 BNE draw2
660 DEC count
670 BNE redo
680 LDA #25
690 JSR oswrch
```

```
700 LDA #6
710 JSR oswrch
720 LDX #4
730 LDY #0
740 .final
750 LDA (param),Y
760 JSR oswrch
770 INY
780 DEX
790 BNE final
800 PLA
810 LDA #0
820 RTS
830 ]
840 NEXT
```

Program 9.8. Implementing OSWORD calls.

figure on the current graphics screen. The program uses the VDU driver OSWRCH to perform the machine code MOVE and PLOTs so that each co-ordinate pair must consist of four bytes. Figure 9.6 shows the parameter block, while Fig. 9.7 shows the four associate line movements needed to draw a rectangle.

The first set of bytes in the parameter block are the MOVE co-ordinates which set the bottom left-hand corner of the square. The next three co-ordinate sets are the DRAW co-ordinates for the first three lines; the last line is drawn to the original MOVE position. The program therefore runs through like this. First a check is made for the correct OSWORD call (lines

```
X,Y       ┌─────────────┐
          │ X1 low      │      OSWORD &A0
          │ X1 high     │      Parameter
          │ Y1 low      │      Block
          │ Y1 high     │
          ├─────────────┤
          │ X2 low      │
          │ X2 high     │
          │ Y2 low      │
          │ Y2 high     │
          ├─────────────┤
          │ X3 low      │
          │ X3 high     │
          │ Y3 low      │
          │ Y3 high     │
          ├─────────────┤
          │ X4 low      │
          │ X4 high     │
          │ Y4 low      │
          │ Y4 high     │
          └─────────────┘
```

Fig. 9.6. The OSWORD &A0 parameter block.

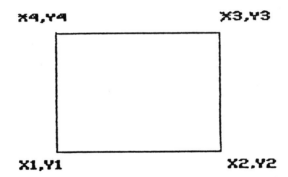

The OSWORD &A0 co-ordinates

Fig. 9.7. The line movements for the OSWORD &A0 call.

340 and 350), and if identified the code proceeds by branching to 'yes' (line 390) otherwise the accumulator is restored and control returned to the MOS (lines 370 and 380).

After selecting the correct VDU code to perform the machine code MOVE (lines 400 to 470), the first set of bytes is extracted from the parameter block to perform the MOVE (lines 490 to 530). A loop is then initialised to read the remaining three sets of co-ordinates from the parameter block and perform the correct set of DRAWs (lines 540 to 710). Lastly, the original set of parameters are extracted to complete the final DRAW command (lines 720 to 790), after which the stack is balanced and control returned to the MOS.

After entering Program 9.8, you might like to try running Program 9.9

```
 10 REM Test OSWORD &A0
 20 REM (C) Bruce Smith
 30 REM The BBC Micro ROM Book
 40 :
 50 X%=&70:Y%=0
 60 FOR loop=0 TO 15
 70 READ byte
 80 X%?loop=byte
 90 NEXT loop
100 MODE 5
110 A%=&A0
120 CALL&FFF1
130 :
140 REM VDU data for shape
150 DATA 100,0,100,0
160 DATA 244,1,100,0
170 DATA 244,1,244,1
180 DATA 100,0,244,1
```

Program 9.9. OSWORD Test.

which will test the validity of the new OSWORD call by drawing a square on a MODE 5 screen.

The Aussie bytes

Implementing an OSBYTE call in a sideways ROM is much simpler as all information is passed to and from call via the index registers only. Program 9.10 implements OSBYTE &70 which, when called, will return the current screen MODE in the X register.

As with OSWORD, the three registers' contents are made available to the

```
 10 REM Implement new OSBYTE call &70
 20 REM to return screen mode only in X
 30 REM (C) Bruce Smith October 1984
 40 REM The BBC Micro ROM Book
 50 :
 60 diff%=&3000
 70 FOR PASS=0 TO 3 STEP 3
 80 P%=&5000
 90 [
100 OPT PASS
110 EQUB 0
120 EQUW 0
130 JMP service_entry+diff%
140 EQUB &82
150 EQUB offset MOD 256
160 EQUB 1
170 .title
180 EQUS "BASIC Tools 1.00"
190 EQUB 0
200 .offset
210 EQUB 0
220 EQUS "(C) Love Byte"
230 EQUB 0
240 .service_entry
250 PHA
260 CMP #7
270 BEQ osbyte
280 PLA
290 RTS
300 :
310 .osbyte
320 LDA &EF
330 CMP #&70
340 BEQ yes
350 PLA
360 RTS
370 .yes
```

```
380 LDX &355
390 STX &F0
400 PLA
410 LDA #0
420 TAY
430 STA &F1
440 RTS
450 ]
460 NEXT
```

Program 9.10. Implementing OSBYTE calls.

routine through zero page locations &EF, &F0 and &F1. After processing the OSBYTE call the values that need be returned to the calling routine *must* be copied into these memory locations as the MOS will then copy these locations into the index registers.

Line by line the program reads like this:

Line 250: Push accumulator onto stack.
Line 260: Is it service call 7?
Line 270: If yes, branch to 'osbyte'.
Line 280: Else pull stack,
Line 290: and return to MOS.
Line 320: GET OSBYTE call code.
Line 330: Is it &70?
Line 340: Branch to 'yes' if it is,
Line 350: else restore stack,
Line 360: and return to MOS.
Line 380: Get current graphics MODE from &355.
Line 390: Write to X register byte.
Line 400: Restore accumulator.
Line 410: Clear accumulator.
Line 420: Move into Y register,
Line 430: and clear Y register byte.
Line 440: Return to MOS.

Program 9.11 provides a short testing routine for you to try once your OSBYTE machine code is established.

```
10 REM Test OSBYTE call &70
20 REM Mode returned in X, Y is zero
30 REM (C) Bruce Smith October 1984
40 REM The BBC Micro ROM Book
50 :
60 A%=&70
70 byte%=USR(&FFF4)
80 mode%=(byte% AND &FF00)/256
90 PRINT"Current screen mode is : MOD
E ";mode%
```

Program 9.11. OSBYTE Test.

Star Trek – the language ROM

Last but certainly not least, the final program of this chapter provides an assembler listing that will allow you to implement a simple language ROM in your sideways ROM or RAM.

The listing provides a hex and ASCII dump routine in the form of a language that is initiated with the command *TREK. Program 9.12 provides the full listing, which should be entered, * SAVEd and *LOADed into sideways RAM for testing and debugging as already described at the start of the chapter.

```
 10 REM Implement a language ROM
 20 REM Monitor TREK
 30 REM call with *TREK
 40 REM (c) Bruce Smith 1984
 50 REM The BBC Micro ROM Book
 60 :
 70 mshigh=&50
 80 mslow=&51
 90 lshigh=&52
100 lslow=&53
110 temp=&54
120 hibyte=&63
130 lobyte=&62
140 hibegin=&61
150 lobegin=&60
160 osrdch=&FFE0
170 osbyte=&FFF4
180 oswrch=&FFEE
190 osnewl=&FFE7
200 osasci=&FFE3
210 comline=&F2
220 diff%=&3000
230 :
240 FOR PASS=0 TO 3 STEP 3
250 P%=&5000
260 [
270 OPT PASS
280 JMP language_entry+diff%
290 JMP service_entry+diff%
300 EQUB &C2
310 EQUB offset MOD 256
320 EQUB 1
330 .title
340 EQUS "Monitor Trek "
350 EQUB 0
360 .offset
370 EQUB 0
380 EQUS "(C) Love Byte"
```

```
390 EQUB O
400 :
410 .service_entry
420 PHA
430 CMP #9
440 BEQ help
450 CMP #4
460 BEQ unrecognised
470 PLA
480 RTS
490 :
500 .help
510 LDX #&FF
520 .helploop
530 INX
540 LDA title+diff%,X
550 JSR osasci
560 BNE helploop
570 JSR osnewl
580 PLA
590 RTS
600 :
610 .unrecognised
620 TYA
630 PHA
640 TXA
650 PHA
660 LDX #&FF
670 DEY
680 .ctloop
690 INX
700 INY
710 LDA table+diff%,X
720 BMI found
730 CMP (comline),Y
740 BEQ ctloop
750 :
760 .nothisrom
770 PLA
780 TAX
790 PLA
800 TAY
810 PLA
820 RTS
830 :
840 .found
850 LDA #&8E
860 LDX &F4
870 JSR &FFF4
880 \ No return!
```

```
 890 :
 900 \ set up Command Table
 910 .table
 920 EQUS "TREK"
 930 EQUB &FF
 940 :
 950 .language_entry
 960 CLI
 970 LDX #&FF
 980 TXS
 990 LDA #22
1000 JSR oswrch
1010 LDA #7
1020 JSR oswrch
1030 LDY #2
1040 LDX #&FF
1050 .langloop
1060 INX
1070 LDA heading+diff%,X
1080 JSR osasci
1090 BNE langloop
1100 :
1110 LDX #&FF
1120 DEY
1130 BNE langloop
1140 .copyloop
1150 INX
1160 LDA copyright+diff%,X
1170 JSR osasci
1180 BNE copyloop
1190 LDA #28
1200 JSR oswrch
1210 LDA #0
1220 JSR oswrch
1230 LDA #24
1240 JSR oswrch
1250 LDA #39
1260 JSR oswrch
1270 LDA #5
1280 JSR oswrch
1290 LDX #&FF
1300 :
1310 .stloop
1320 INX
1330 LDA start+diff%,X
1340 JSR osasci
1350 BNE stloop
1360 JSR inputaddr+diff%
1370 LDA hibyte
1380 STA hibegin
```

```
1390 LDA lobyte
1400 STA lobegin
1410 :
1420 LDX #&FF
1430 .endloop
1440 INX
1450 LDA end+diff%,X
1460 JSR osasci
1470 BNE endloop
1480 JSR inputaddr+diff%
1490 LDA #13
1500 JSR osasci
1510 :
1520 .nextline
1530 JSR address+diff%
1540 LDY #0
1550 LDX #7
1560 .hexloop
1570 LDA (lobegin),Y
1580 JSR hexout+diff%
1590 JSR space+diff%
1600 INY
1610 DEX
1620 BPL hexloop
1630 LDA #134
1640 JSR oswrch
1650 :
1660 LDY #0
1670 LDX #7
1680 .ascloop
1690 LDA (lobegin),Y
1700 CMP #32
1710 BCC spot
1720 CMP #128
1730 BCC jumpover
1740 .spot
1750 LDA #ASC(".")
1760 .jumpover
1770 JSR oswrch
1780 INY
1790 DEX
1800 BPL ascloop
1810 :
1820 LDA #&0D
1830 JSR osasci
1840 CLC
1850 LDA lobegin
1860 ADC #8
1870 STA lobegin
1880 BCC nocarry
```

```
1890 INC hibegin
1900 .nocarry
1910 LDA lobegin
1920 CMP lobyte
1930 BCC nextline
1940 LDA hibegin
1950 CMP hibyte
1960 BCC nextline
1970 :
1980 JSR osnewl
1990 LDX #&FF
2000 .goonloop
2010 INX
2020 LDA continue+diff%,X
2030 JSR oswrch
2040 BNE goonloop
2050 .testkey
2060 JSR osrdch
2070 CMP #ASC("Y")
2080 BNE skipover
2090 JMP language_entry+diff%
2100 .skipover
2110 CMP #ASC("N")
2120 BNE testkey
2130 :
2140 LDA #26
2150 JSR oswrch
2160 LDA #12
2170 JSR oswrch
2180 LDA #&BB
2190 JSR osbyte
2200 LDA #&8E
2210 JMP osbyte
2220 :
2230 \ machine code subroutines
2240 :
2250 .inputaddr
2260 JSR characters+diff%
2270 LDA mshigh
2280 JSR check+diff%
2290 ASL A
2300 ASL A
2310 ASL A
2320 ASL A
2330 STA temp
2340 LDA mslow
2350 JSR check+diff%
2360 ORA temp
2370 STA hibyte
2380 LDA lshigh
2390 JSR check+diff%
```

```
2400 ASL A
2410 ASL A
2420 ASL A
2430 ASL A
2440 STA temp
2450 LDA lslow
2460 JSR check+diff%
2470 ORA temp
2480 STA lobyte
2490 RTS
2500 :
2510 .characters
2520 JSR osrdch
2530 JSR osasci
2540 STA mshigh
2550 JSR osrdch
2560 STA mslow
2570 JSR osasci
2580 JSR osrdch
2590 JSR osasci
2600 STA lshigh
2610 JSR osrdch
2620 JSR osasci
2630 STA lslow
2640 RTS
2650 :
2660 .check
2670 CMP #58
2680 BCS atof
2690 AND #15
2700 RTS
2710 .atof
2720 SBC #55
2730 RTS
2740 :
2750 .space
2760 LDA #32
2770 JMP oswrch
2780 :
2790 .address
2800 LDA #129
2810 JSR oswrch
2820 LDX #lobegin
2830 LDA 1,X
2840 JSR hexout+diff%
2850 LDA 0,X
2860 JSR hexout+diff%
2870 LDA #130
2880 JSR oswrch
2890 RTS
2900 :
```

```
2910 .hexout
2920 PHA
2930 LSR A
2940 LSR A
2950 LSR A
2960 LSR A
2970 JSR digit+diff%
2980 PLA
2990 .digit
3000 AND #15
3010 CMP #10
3020 BCC no
3030 ADC #6
3040 .no
3050 ADC #48
3060 JMP oswrch
3070 :
3080 \ ASCII string storage area
3090 :
3100 .copyright
3110 EQUD &20202086
3120 EQUB &20
3130 EQUS "(C) LoveByte Soft  1984"
3140 EQUB 13
3150 EQUB 0
3160 .heading
3170 EQUB 141
3180 EQUB 131
3190 EQUD &20202020
3200 EQUD &20202020
3210 EQUS "MONITOR TREK"
3220 EQUB 13
3230 EQUB 0
3240 EQUB 141
3250 .start
3260 EQUB 130
3270 EQUS "Start :&"
3280 EQUB 129
3290 EQUB 0
3300 .end
3310 EQUB 130
3320 EQUS "    End   :&"
3330 EQUB 129
3340 EQUB 0
3350 .continue
3360 EQUB 130
3370 EQUS "Go again (Y/N)? "
3380 EQUB 0
3390 ]NEXT
```

Program 9.12. Implementing a language ROM.

Once entered, the display screen clears and the title and copyright strings are displayed. A text window is set up which ensures that these items remain on screen throughout the languages operation. You are then prompted to enter a start and end address in hexadecimal format – note that the '&' is already provided so you need only enter the hex digits themselves. Once this has occurred, the area of memory between these two addresses is dumped to the screen. The format for each line is the current address, followed by the eight bytes from this address displayed in hex, and then again in ASCII form. If the byte is not displayable ASCII then a full-stop is displayed in its place. The listing may be halted at any time by using the CTRL-SHIFT key combination in the usual manner.

When the listing has completed you will be asked whether you wish to display a further area of memory. Pressing Y will reset the language and the process will repeat, otherwise BASIC will be re-entered.

Now for the listing description. The first 22 lines set up the variables required by the language to operate, namely operating system calls and zero page storage for vectored addresses.

The ROM header is assembled in lines 280 to 390. The header is much the same as those described for service ROMs but differences do occur. A language entry jump address must be assembled into the first three ROM header bytes (line 280); the ROM type value must also be amended to include the now set language bit, bit 6, therefore the byte to be assembled is 11000010, or &C2 hex; line 300 takes care of this. Finally, the title string in line 340 has been amended. A service entry point, and therefore interpreter, must also be included to handle any *HELP service requests and unrecognised command requests. This is assembled by lines 410 to 880.

The unrecognised command we are testing for is *TREK and this is looked for by lines 610 to 740. A branch to 'found' is performed if the *TREK command is recognised, and the language entered through the language entry point by executing OSBYTE &8E (lines 840 to 870).

The language entry point is entered via the JMP instruction located at &8000, which is in effect a jump to line 950. First things first, however: the MOS must be reset by re-enabling interrupts with CLI, followed closely by resetting of the stack (lines 960 to 980). To see just how important these processes are, try omiting these lines and running the reassembled code!

The teletext mode screen is selected and the double height title message printed (lines 990 to 1130). After printing the more normal sized copyright message the new text window is defined (lines 1110 to 1280), which resets the top of the screen to five rows down. Lines 1290 to 1640 then request you to input the start and end addresses for the dump, which begins at 'nextline', line 1520.

After the current line start address has been displayed (line 1530) the following eight bytes are displayed in hex (lines 1540 to 1620) followed by the same eight bytes in ASCII form (lines 1660 to 1800). A line feed is issued (lines 1820 to 1830) and then eight is added to the current address value (lines

1840 to 1930). If the start address is equal to or greater than the end address, the 'Go again (Y/N)?' prompt is issued (lines 2050 to 2120). If Y is pressed the above code is simply re-entered. If, on the other hand, N is printed, BASIC must be re-entered. To do this the screen is set to its default value (lines 2140 to 2170), the BASIC ROM number is found using OSBYTE &BB and is re-entered in the usual way with OSBYTE &8E (lines 2180 to 2210). The assembler from 2250 to 3380 sets up the various input/output and conversion routines, plus the ASCII string tables used by the main program as follows:

Lines 2250 to 2490: Get four characters from the keyboard, convert them into two two-byte binary numbers and save them in two zero page vectors.
Lines 2510 to 2640: Called by the above routine to read and echo the keyboard.
Lines 2660 to 2730: Convert an ASCII hex digit into a four-bit binary number.
Lines 2750 to 2770: Print a single space.
Lines 2790 to 2890: Print the contents of two bytes as a two-byte ASCII hexadecimal number.
Lines 2910 to 3060: Print the byte in the accumulator as a two-digit hexadecimal value. This routine is called twice by the address printing subroutine.
Lines 3100 to 3370: Set up ASCII strings and control characters.

As it stands, the program listing is simple for the purpose of explanation and understanding. For example, the BRK vector should really be reset to an error handler held within our own ROM. As it stands, the ROM is incapable of producing an error so we get away with it; any expansion will no doubt require you to add one. While on the subject of error handling, the address input routine does not perform any check for illegal hexadecimal characters. The program will still work, however, as only the relevant bits are used from the illegal character, so entering KKKK will result in &7777 being used as the address. Finally, no provision for the use of OS commands has been made, so use of the filing system is not possible.

Chapter Ten
ROM and Board

Four sideways ROM sockets are available on the Beeb – two, if you discount
BASIC and a DFS – but your personal ROM collection will probably
exceed this (my own ROM collection numbers about thirty at present!). The
MOS firmware has been designed to handle up to sixteen sideways ROMs.
Many commercial concerns have been quick to jump on the hardware band-
waggon, producing a variety of sideways ROM expansion boards.
Interestingly enough, this is one area where Acorn have no development
plans, nor are they likely to. The official Acorn line is that they 'will make no
comments on the subject of sideways ROM expansion boards'!

As with the purchase of sideways ROMs, it is very much a personal affair
and the choice of ROM board should be based on the factors that you
yourself consider to be important. In this chapter I will try to examine the

Fig. 10.1. ROM and board!

various aspects of board design that should be considered, look at a few boards that have been supplied to me by manufacturers – each offering something different – and then finally provide the constructional details for a simple, inexpensive, multi-ROM board.

Inside out

One of the first considerations must be whether you want your ROM board to be mounted inside or outside the Beeb's case? Many ROM boards do not allow you a choice whereas a few do. Both methods have advantages. Internal boards require you to remove the lid whenever you want to add or extract a ROM. They also increase the amount of heat inside the Beeb which could affect the operation of the other components, particularly the video ULA, the early models of which are prone to overheating and are supplied with a heat-sink attached to dissipate its own heat. Fitting the board internally will often require the removal and remounting of either the 6502 or the MOS and other chips. Sometimes you will even be required to solder wires onto links or other chips. The link aspect is also interesting, as several of the selectable links present on early issue boards, say issue 3, have been removed or made permanent on later issue boards, such as issue 7.

Boards that mount externally will normally only require two connections internally. Usually they plug into the 6502 microprocessor socket which relocates on the main board or a piggy-back board mounted internally, and a wire to a selectable link aids with the ROM decoding. Boards mounted outside are obviously more accessible, allowing chips to be added and removed readily. However, they must be placed safely outside the Beeb and preferably covered in some way to prevent accidental mechanical damage, dust accumulating and spillage of coffee (yes, that's happened to me!).

Finally, will the board need to co-exist with a sideways RAM or double density disc interface? If so, is it compatible?

Designer genes

The design and production of a ROM extension board is of paramount importance, and must be assessed carefully before you purchase a particular brand. You have spent a great deal of cash on your micro and the extra few pounds required for a well-designed and professionally produced board are well worth while.

Checking a board is really quite simple and no real electronic expertise is required. A look at the BBC Micro printed circuit board (PCB) will give you a good indication of what you are looking for. The board itself should be of glass-fibre construction, and the tracks should be neatly 'cut' and polished, and lacquered to prevent spoiling. Have a look on the underside of the PCB.

Is there any sign of wire links running from one side of a track to another that has obviously been added as an after-thought. Similarly, are there any components on this side of the board, other than plugs, such as capacitors? While the odd wire jumper link may be inevitable, several of these and the use of capacitors on the underside of a board indicate poor design.

On the board's component side, take a good look at the ROM sockets. Are they of good quality and will they withstand ROMs being inserted and extracted? Also, how easy will it be to lever the ROM out at a later stage?

Check as far as you can that the components are soldered correctly into place. Also, see that each component is labelled on the board by some means, preferably by silk-screened lettering. You will need to know what each ROM socket number is. Many boards offer link selectable operations and battery backup so you will need to know which is what.

It is important to assure yourself that the board is fully buffered, so that the Beeb is fully protected from the expansion board and any misuse of it. Ask the supplier or shop assistant to confirm this.

Do you require the board to hold sideways RAM? Check out this aspect if so.

Will you be changing ROMs frequently, switching between BASICs or disc filing systems, for example? If so, inclusion of an on-board ZIF (Zero Insertion Force) socket is important.

The Beeb can handle three sizes of EPROM, namely 4K, 8K and 16K. Will you need access to these size chips and if so will your choice of board handle them?

Hopefully, some of these pointers will help you in your personal board selection. My own choice? Well, my perfect ROM board has yet to be produced. If it does ever materialise it will have 16 sockets, all capable of holding any size EPROM, all capable of holding RAM, and be completely software and hardware selectable so that ROMs may be switched in and out of circuit as required, with LEDs indicating the state of each socket. The board will also contain at least three ZIF sockets, be fully enclosed by a Beeb matching box with an easy access list, and – obviously – mounted externally.

My home use of expansion boards is limited to just two, the APTL Sidewise board, and the Micro Pulse ROM Box. I'm lucky enough to own two Beebs, one of which I use for programming and the other is an almost-dedicated word processor. The programming Beeb has the APTL fitted with a full complement of ROMs and 8K of sideways RAM. I bought this board as the best buy about a couple of years ago and it has performed exceptionally since that time. It does lack the ZIF socket for easy change of ROMs, but I have overcome this problem by using the extension socket project detailed at the end of this chapter.

The other Beeb, being used almost entirely as a word processor, does not require the use of multiple ROMs, but the four sockets provided are limited to BASIC, DFS, Wordwise and View. I also like to use this Beeb for programming in languages other than BASIC so I find the external Micro

Pulse ROM Box ideal for switching in ROMs. But these are my personal choices – you must make up your own mind to ensure that the board you choose will suit your own requirements completely.

Aries B12

The Aries B12 sideways ROM expansion board implements 12 of the 16 possible sideways ROMs and also includes two sockets into which a bank of RAM up to 16K long may be added in the form of two 8K RAM chips.

The expansion board takes the form of three boards, supplied packed in polystyrene foam with a well illustrated manual. Fitting is straightforward and no difficult problems should be encountered. The first stage involves the removal of all the sideways ROMs present in the four on-board sockets. Into their place a base board must be fitted simply by aligning its pins over the two end sockets and pushing it firmly home.

Next, the adaptor board must be fitted into the socket allocated to the 6502 microprocessor, which is refitted onto the adaptor board itself. This board may already be fitted if you are using the Aries B20 RAM board.

Your sideways ROMs can be placed onto the ROM board. The highest priority socket on the board is number 12.

The final stage in the assembly is to link the three boards together using the easily distinguishable ribbon cables.

The Aries B12 board may be mounted internally or externally, either on

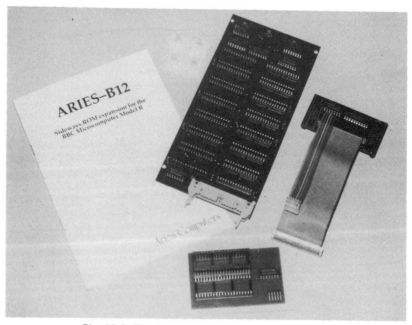

Fig. 10.2. The Aries B12 sideways ROM board.

the underside of the computer's lid or on top or behind the Beeb. Sticky feet are provided for these purposes.

As already mentioned, RAM may be added to two special sockets on the board. The RAM chips are the 6264 8K by 8 static RAMs, and ROM filing system or sideways ROM software may be loaded using the *LOAD command. The Aries board is produced by Aries Computers.

APTL Sidewise

The APTL Sidewise board is an internally mounted board which allows the full complement of 16 sideways ROMs to be implemented: four in the normal Beeb sockets and 12 on the APTL board. Up to 16K of sideways RAM may also be installed.

Fitting the board is simple enough but requires some care. First the MOS ROM in IC51 and the A/D converter chip, IC73, must be removed. If the A/D chip is not present the board will still work. These two chips (one if the A/D is absent) must then be inserted into their corresponding sockets on the Sidewise board. A two-wire fly lead dangling from the Sidewise board must then be attached to the lower half of link S21. The connector pins at either end of the Sidewise board must now be aligned over the IC73 and IC51 sockets and carefully pushed into place.

ROM number 15 is divided into two sockets, 15a and 15b, which will

Fig. 10.3. The APTL Sidewise board in position with a near full complement of ROMs. The two empty sockets will take ROM or RAM.

accept 8K RAM chips. By purchasing a special kit it is possible to add a battery-backed RAM option, thereby allowing RAM contents to remain even when the Beeb is switched off. For this battery-backed option to be used, low standby power consumption RAMs such as TC556LPs should be used. For normal operations, standard 2764 RAM chips may be used as normal.

Eight selectable links are available on the Sidewise board to allow various other options to be selected, such as battery-backed RAM and readdressing of RAM chips.

Exprom

The Exprom board is produced by Anderson Electronics and is very versatile, allowing up to 16 on-board ROMs of 2K, 4K, 8K or 16K in size, in addition to 8K or 16K RAM chips. The board is installed by repositioning the 6502 microprocessor onto the Exprom board and fitting the plug connector on its ribbon cable into the vacated processor socket. A single wire connection to the centre pin of link S19 (not present on my issue 7 board, but present on issue 3 boards!) from the Exprom board completes the connections.

Sideways ROMs present on the BBC board must be removed and transferred to the Exprom board, which may then be mounted inside or outside the Beeb's case using the sticky feet provided.

Each of the 16 ROM sockets have associated links which, when made in a particular direction, will define the operation of that socket. ROM sockets 4 to 15 are equipped to handle ROMs or EPROMs of 4K or greater capacity as supplied. By altering link settings (very easily done) the 4K size may be selected on any of these sockets.

ROM sockets 0 to 3 are equipped to handle RAM, EPROM and ROM in 2K, 4K, 8K or 16K chips. Additionally, these sockets may also be arranged to provide a contiguous address within the 16K paged ROM/RAM space. As an optional extra, a ZIF socket may be installed in the ROM number 4 position.

The manual supplied with the Exprom board is extremely imformative and full of technical information about the board and combination possibilities.

ROM Box

The ROM Box by Micro Pulse is an externally positioned affair, that allows up to eight sideways ROMs, in addition to three mounted internally, to be used. The fourth internal sideways ROM socket is used to make the connection between Beeb and external Box.

The ROM Box is also different in that only one of the eight possible

Fig. 10.4. The Micro Pulse ROM Box.

external ROMs may be used at once. This is achieved by switching it 'in' by means of a rotary knob. The paged-in ROM is signified by an illuminated LED at the head of the relevant chip. ROM socket number 5 is a ZIF socket allowing multiple changes of frequently changed ROMs. The ROM Box is fully enclosed in a sturdy Beeb-matching metal Box and access to the ROMs is via a hinged perspex lid. The ROM Box is very simple to install and operate and this adds to its appeal. It is not possible to use RAM in any of the ROM sockets, however.

Sideways ROM cartridge

This is a rather innovative method of multi-ROM implementation. The Viglen package comes supplied with an extension cable and cartridge. The extension cable is fitted with a 28-way socket at one end and a ROM cartridge socket at the other end. The 28-pin socket is fitted into a vacant sideways ROM socket on the Beeb and the ribbon cable is passed across the front of the Beeb and under the keyboard. The cartridge socket is then pushed through the perforated area on the left of the keyboard fascia, which has become known as the 'ashtray', and clips into place!

ROMs, 8K or 16K, can then be fixed into individual ROM cartridges which can be sealed inside by reassembling the two halves of the cartridge and securing them with a screw.

To use the ROM, the cartridge is pushed into the socket and the Beeb switched on, or if already on, BREAK is pressed. By acquiring extra ROM

Fig. 10.5. The Viglen ROM cartridge in use.

cartridges a whole library of sideways ROM cartridges can be assembled and used as the need arises.

DIY extension ROM box

A very simple but, nevertheless, very effective ROM extension socket can be home-built for about ten pounds. The extension socket simply consists of a ZIF socket mounted on a small piece of veroboard, housed in a suitable box, that plugs into a sideways ROM socket via a suitable length of ribbon cable. When in position, ROMs can be inserted into the ZIF socket as and when required.

To construct the box you'll need the following items of hardware. All are readily available items:

1 × 28 pin ZIF socket
1 × 28 pin IDC header plug
1 × 12 inch length 28-way ribbon cable
1 × 0.1μF ceramic capacitor
1 × 1μF 16V tantalum bead capacitor
1 × box to suit
1 × strip veroboard to suit box size
2 × mounting screws and nuts.

Figure 10.6 shows how simply everything connects together, while Fig. 10.7 illustrates the final ROM extension box.

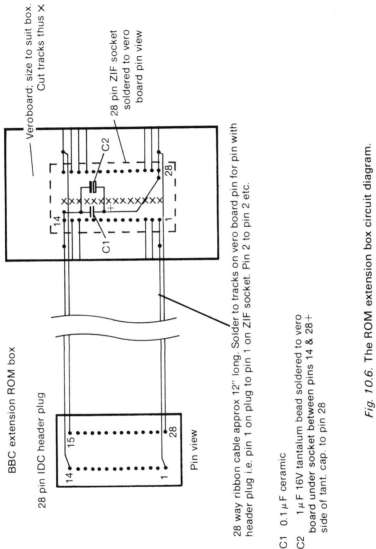

Fig. 10.6. The ROM extension box circuit diagram.

The ZIF socket should first be mounted onto some veroboard, and tracks cut as indicated in Fig. 10.6. The two capacitors go between pins 14 and 28 of the ZIF socket, ensuring that the positive side of the tantalum bead capacitor is to pin 28.

I have found that a foot length of ribbon cable is the best length and each end of this should be soldered pin to pin, i.e. pin 1 on the ZIF to pin 1 on the header. Finally, the ZIF board can be mounted in a suitable box using a couple of nuts and screws.

To use the Extension Box you will need to gain access to the sideways

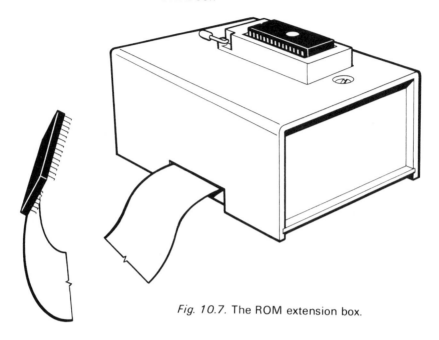

Fig. 10.7. The ROM extension box.

ROM sockets and insert the header plug as though it were a sideways ROM – ensuring correct orientation. Trail the lead to the right of the Beeb over the edge of the case and reassemble. To insert a ROM, first turn off the Beeb and place the chip in the socket with pin 1 towards the ZIF socket lever. Push the lever down to shut the ZIF socket and power up your Beeb. Changing ROMs is just as simple – turn off the Beeb, and replace the ROM in the ROM extension socket!

Sideways RAM

The importance of sideways RAM cannot be stressed enough in the development of software to reside in the paged ROM area. Writing code to sit in this area of memory, that works correctly with the operating system, with any other ROMs present, and does what it is supposed to do itself is not always as straightforward as it seems. Very few programmers can write a machine code program of any length that will work correctly first time, and even less so when it is to sit in the paged ROM area. Your coding will therefore need to go through several stages of development – with each stage needing testing *in situ*. Sideways RAM allows you to *LOAD or, in some implementations, write your code directly to it, thus making it readily available to you. Without sideways RAM each stage of development would need to be programmed, or 'blown', into an EPROM before testing, and then presumably erased before going on to the next stage of development or ironing out any bugs.

Fig. 10.8. The Solidisk sideways RAM.

There are basically two ways that sideways RAM systems can be purchased. The first is to purchase a sideways ROM board that allows the user to utilise one of the ROM sockets to hold RAM, preferably up to 16K, or secondly to purchase a sideways RAM system, such as the system marketed by Solidisk Technology.

The Solidisk system comes in many shapes and sizes, from 16K to 256K of sideways RAM. A comprehensive manual and copious amounts of software to use with the Solidisk are also provided.

Fitting the system is not a job for the faint-hearted but should not present problems to anyone who feels confident in handling EPROMs and chips in general.

The Solidisk (I am describing the 32K unit) consists of three items, the base unit, the RAM unit and the mini-ROM cartridge. The base unit plugs into the Beeb's right-most sideways ROM socket. This unit has a socket on the top of it that will accept both the mini ROM cartridge and the main RAM bank. In addition, three sets of wires (in bunches of six wires, three wires and two wires) are used to implement the RAM decoding and read-write lines. These sets of wires must be connected as follows:

3 wires to the 6522 (IC69)
2 wires to 74LS163 (IC76)
2 wires to the 6502 (IC1)
4 wires to links S20 and S22

Inserting the wires into corresponding pin sockets for each chip is more fiddly than technically difficult. All that is now required is to insert the RAM board to use the sideways RAM system.

The mini-ROM cartridge allows you to insert ROMs rather than the sideways RAM into the right-hand socket position.

Solidisk point out that their system is not compatible with any make of sideways ROM board. This is not really the case as I have managed, with some good old-fashioned jiggery-pokery, to install the system and use it with the APTL board – but it is difficult and not to be recommended, so I'm not going to tell you how!

This 'incompatibility' need not be a problem as you can save your sideways ROMs to disc and simply load them into a sideways RAM bank as required, using the programs supplied with the system.

Cordon bleu

Keeping track of what ROMs you are using inside your Beeb at any one time is reasonably simple – just type *HELP. However, over-zealous firmware writers often put too much detail into their *HELP response messages, so much so that if you are using all sixteen ROM sockets on an expansion board the *HELP listing can fly across the screen, producing up to three screens of *HELP information!

The program presented here will provide a neatly listed screen of information, telling you what ROM is in which socket, and will also print the ROM code, so that you can tell at a glance whether it is a language or a service ROM.

Program 10.1 provides the assembler details. When RUN, the machine

```
 10 REM Sideways Rom Menu
 20 REM (C) Bruce Smith
 30 REM September 1984
 40 REM The BBC Micro ROM Book
 50 :
 60 ROM=&8000
 70 romselect=&FE30
 80 vector=&70
 90 oswrch=&FFEE
100 osasci=&FFE3
110 osbyte=&FFF4
120 :
130 FOR pass=0 TO 3 STEP 3
140 P%=&900
150 [             OPT pass
160 .start
170             JSR setup
180             LDX romselect
190             STX basic
200             LDA #0
210             :
220 .mainloop
230             STA romcount
```

```
              LDA #&86
              JSR osbyte
              STY ypos
              LDA #31
              JSR oswrch
              LDA #3
              JSR oswrch
              TYA
              JSR oswrch
              LDA romcount
              JSR hexout
              LDA romcount
              STA romselect
              LDA #&80
              STA vector+1
              LDA #0
              STA vector
              LDY #7
              LDA (vector),Y
430           STA vector
440           LDY #2
450           LDA (vector),Y
460           CMP #ASC("C")
470           BNE norom
480           LDA #31
490           JSR oswrch
500           LDA #8
510           JSR oswrch
520           LDA ypos
530           JSR oswrch
540           LDY #8
550 .loop
560           LDA romcount
570           STA romselect
580           LDA ROM+6
590           STA type
600           INY
610           LDA ROM,Y
620           JSR oswrch
630           BNE loop
640 .endtitle
650           LDA #31
660           JSR oswrch
670           LDA #33
680           JSR oswrch
690           LDA ypos
700           JSR oswrch
710           LDA type
720           JSR hexout
730 .norom
```

```
 740                JSR &FFE7
 750                LDY romcount
 760                INY
 770                TYA
 780                CMP #16
 790                BEQ finished
 800                JMP mainloop
 810 .finished
 820                LDA basic
 830                STA romselect
 840                RTS
 850                :
 860 .basic
 870                EQUB 0
 880 .romcount
 890                EQUB 0
 900 .ypos
 910                EQUB 0
 920 .type
 930                EQUB 0
 940                :
 950 .hexout
 960                PHA
 970                LSR A
 980                LSR A
 990                LSR A
1000                LSR A
1010                JSR digit
1020                PLA
1030 .digit
1040                AND #15
1050                CMP #10
1060                BCC over
1070                ADC #6
1080 .over
1090                ADC #48
1100                JMP oswrch
1110                :
1120 .setup
1130                LDA #22
1140                JSR oswrch
1150                LDA #7
1160                JSR oswrch
1170                LDY #2
1180 .next
1190                LDX #&FF
1200 .heading
1210                INX
1220                LDA ascii,X
1230                JSR osasci
```

```
1240              BNE heading
1250              DEY
1260              BNE next
1270              JSR &FFE7
1280              RTS
1290              :
1300 .ascii
1310              EQUB 141
1320              EQUB 129
1330              EQUD &20202020
1340              EQUW &2020
1350              EQUS "Sideways ROM Menu"
1360              EQUB 13
1370              EQUB 0
1380 ]
1390 NEXT
1400 *KEY 0 CALL &900!M
```

Program 10.1. Sideways ROM menu.

code is placed at &900. Obviously, this value can be altered to suit your own needs as required. The program works by reading each ROM in turn, obtaining its title from the header title string and the ROM type from the byte at &8006 in the ROM.

As listed, the program is written to handle all sixteen possible sockets. If you are only using the four on the Beeb's main board then the sixteen in line 780 should be changed to four.

A brief line by line description of the program now follows:

Lines 10 to 40: Program details.
Lines 60 to 110: Initialise variables.
Line 170: Set up screen and print heading.
Lines 180 to 190: Get BASIC's ROM number and save it.
Line 200: Set ROM number counter.
Line 230: Save current ROM count.
Lines 240 to 320: Reposition text cursor to start of new line.
Lines 330 to 340: Print current ROM number.
Lines 350 to 360: Program ROM select register to select this ROM.
Lines 370 to 400: Set up zero page vector to point to start of ROM.
Line 410: Initialise indexing register to point to copyright offset pointer.
Lines 450 to 460: Read this byte and test for ASC ("C").
Line 470: If this byte is not ASC ("C") then no ROM is present so branch to 'norom'.
Lines 480 to 530: Else move text cursor across the screen ready to print out ROM title string.
Line 540: Initialise indexing register to point to title string.
Lines 560 to 570: Reselect ROM by programming select register.
Lines 580 to 590: Extract ROM type number and save.

Lines 600 to 630: Print ASCII title string until terminating zero encountered.

Lines 650 to 700: Tab text cursor along line.

Lines 710 to 720: Print ROM type value.

Line 740: Perform a line feed.

Lines 750 to 760: Increment ROM count.

Lines 770 to 780: Move it across into the accumulator and compare with total ROMs present.

Line 790: If equal then branch to 'finish'.

Line 800: Else jump back to 'mainloop' to go again.

Lines 820 to 840: Reselect BASIC and return to it!

Lines 860 to 930: Variable storage area.

Lines 950 to 1100: Binary to ASCII hexadecimal conversion and printing routine.

Lines 1120 to 1280: Select MODE 7 and print heading.

Lines 1300 to 1370: Control characters and ASCII string storage area.

Now you see me...

With the vast amount of ROM firmware around these days it is inevitable that commands will 'clash'. In other words, two ROMs will use the same command name. This is fine if the command you want to use is installed in the higher priority ROM but if it is the lower priority ROM then it is difficult to access. Unless the ROM has a special prefix letter, the B associated with TOOLKIT commands, for example, then the only sure fire way to get at it is to rearrange the ROMs in their respective sockets.

There is a software solution to this problem. When the MOS performs its unrecognised command service call, it first looks in the ROM type table at &2A1 (OS1.2) to see what sockets contain ROMs, and passes the service call to these ROMs only. If the ROM type byte contains a zero then that ROM socket is by-passed. The software solution then is to write a zero into the clashing ROM's type byte in this table! Program 10.2 is the one you need to enter for this. When called, it will ask you for the number of the socket containing the ROM, this should be entered as a hex digit without the prefix &. In other words, the value entered should be 0, 1, 2, 3, 4, 5, 6, 7, 8, 9, A, B, C, D, E, or F. The socket number can be obtained using the Menu program given above. The program will then read the address of the ROM type table and write a zero into the relevant location. Note that the table will be reset to its normal condition simply by hitting the BREAK key.

The listing should be straightforward, but a line by liner is included here for completeness:

Line 130: Set absolute indexing register.

Lines 150 to 180: Print prompt string.

```
  10 REM Sideways ROM disabler
  20 REM (c) Bruce Smith
  30 REM September 1984
  40 REM The BBC Micro ROM Book
  50 :
  60 osasci=&FFE3
  70 osword=&FFF4
  80 osbyte=&FFF4
  90 vector=&70
 100 FOR pass=0 TO 3 STEP 3
 110 P%=&A00
 120 [OPT pass
 130 LDX #&FF
 140 .loop
 150 INX
 160 LDA ascii,X
 170 JSR osasci
 180 BNE loop
 190 JSR &FFE0
 200 JSR osasci
 210 CMP #58
 220 BCS atof
 230 AND #15
 240 BCC over
 250 .atof
 260 SBC #55
 270 .over
 280 PHA
 290 LDA #170
 300 LDX #0
 310 LDY #255
 320 JSR osbyte
 330 STY vector+1
 340 STX vector
 350 PLA
 360 TAY
 365 LDA #0
 370 STA (vector),Y
 380 RTS
 390 .ascii
 400 EQUS "Enter ROM Number :&0"
 410 EQUB 0
 420 ]
 430 NEXT
```

Program 10.2. Sideways ROM disabler.

Lines 190 to 260: Read a hexadecimal ASCII character from the keyboard and convert to binary.

Line 280: Save binary value on stack.

Lines 290 to 340: Read address of ROM type table and place in a zero page vector.

Lines 250 to 260: Restore ROM socket number and index from stack and move into Y register.

Lines 370 to 390: Write zero into relevant byte and return to BASIC.

Chapter Eleven
Blow Your Own

Once you have a fully debugged program ready to take its place in the paged area of the Beeb's memory map, there are only two courses open to you as regards its use. First, you can keep it on disc and load it into your sideways RAM as and when you need it. If you have a large RAM capacity system such as the Solidisk this is quite feasible as you still have extra paged memory banks available for other sideways programs to be loaded in and used.

If, on the other hand, you have only a single area of sideways RAM available and you are going to need frequent access to it, then the second option is to program an EPROM so that this can be inserted into your Beeb and be permanently on tap.

Programming an EPROM is really simplicity itself and no prior knowledge of electronics is needed since most commercial EPROM programmers are extremely easy to use. In fact, virtually all the hardware you need to program an EPROM, or *blow* an EPROM as it is usually called, is on the other side of the Beeb's user port in the form of the 6522 VIA.

Make or break?

If you are going to blow your own, then an EPROM programmer is now a highly desirable piece of equipment. As already stated, an EPROM programmer in its simplest form consists of only a few items of hardware – the donkey work being performed by the 6522 VIA and the software needed to transfer bytes from memory to the user port. The decision now arises as to whether you wish to buy a commercial EPROM programmer or build one yourself. If you are at all practical then the prospect of building your own programmer will certainly appeal and to that end a circuit diagram and suitable software is provided here. Otherwise you will need to part with some hard-earned cash to purchase a suitable programmer, although this will not necessarily break the bank. As with most purchases in life, it is best to sit down with pen and paper and make a few notes as to what you will require from the programmer. A few examples might be helpful. Will you be producing your EPROM in numbers, perhaps for resale or as giveaways to friends? In that case you would need an EPROM programmer that has the facility for this and perhaps a few programming sockets, thereby reducing the actual time required to program each EPROM (which can take between one and ten minutes depending on the software and various other factors).

If you are only programming EPROMs on an occasional basis, one or two at a time for home use, then purchasing the above type of programmer would be a waste of money, as you only require the bare essentials. Will you need to program varying sizes of EPROM, i.e. 4K, 8K and 16K? If so, the programmer must be capable of doing so – many can't. Is your user port in constant use? If so, you are probably better off looking for an EPROM programmer that can be attached onto the 1MHz bus, and *vice versa*.

Does the software handle everything or do you have to oversee the operation by turning knobs and flicking switches as and when prompted? The type of software supplied with the programmer is also an important consideration. Will it allow you to copy, verify and program an EPROM? Will it format ROM images and allow you to program an EPROM in the ROM filing system format? Will it test for a blank EPROM? Will it provide you with a checksum? Will the software work with both the cassette filing system and disc filing system?

Again, look at what's on offer and decide what you need; there's little point in paying extra cash for software you're never going to use. A good source of names and addresses of EPROM programmer retailers is your favourite computer magazine (*Acorn User*, of course!). Just look through the adverts and see just what is on offer. The price? Well, a simple EPROM programmer and software will cost you at least twenty pounds which really is pretty good value for money.

DIY

> **Important**
> Evert effort has been made to ensure that the information supplied is accurate and reliable. However, no liability can be assumed on the part of the author or the publishers for incorrect use resulting in damage to any equipment, or personal accident, or consequential loss in any form whatsoever.

Constructing your own programmer is straightforward enough, and anybody with a little soldering iron experience should have no problems. The cost of producing the DIY programmer will vary depending on whether you have any materials to hand or not. Starting from scratch, about fifteen pounds should be adequate, and the bulk of this will be spent on the zero insertion force (ZIF) socket and ribbon cable and connectors. However, you will need to have access to a power supply that is capable of giving you 21V (± 0.5V) at 30mA in addition to a 5V source. The 5V supply could be extracted from the Beeb's auxiliary power output socket. Fig. 11.1 shows a suitable circuit for extracting 21V @ 30mA supply. *This circuit contains a mains electricity supply which can be lethal if not handled and housed*

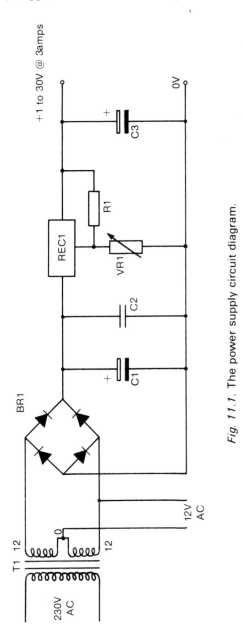

Fig. 11.1. The power supply circuit diagram.

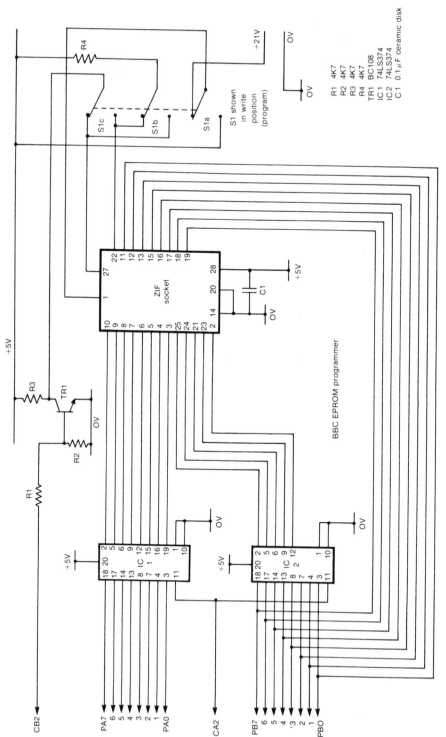

Fig. 11.2. The EPROM programmer circuit diagram.

correctly. If in doubt consult a qualified electrician. A box to place the programmer in will also be required but just about anything will do. Believe it or not, my programmer is housed in an unusual plastic Nesquick (yes, the milk shake) container I bought in the Far East two years ago!

Your parts shopping list is as follows:

1 × 28 pin ZIF socket
2 × 74LS374
4 × 4.7K 0.25W HS carbon film resistors
1 × 0.1μF ceramic disc capacitor
1 × BC108 transistor
2 × 20-pin DIL sockets
1 × 3-pole change-over toggle switch
1 × 26-way, PCB header plug
1 × 20-way, PCB header plug
1 × length of ribbon cable (as short as possible)
1 × 0.1 inch grid veroboard (a 6 inch strip should be enough)
1 × length of tinned copper wire
1 × length of solder
1 × suitable box

The size of veroboard and the length of tinned copper wire and solder you need will depend on your own expertise. I use copious amounts purely because I'm not particularly neat when it comes to constructing veroboards!

Figure 11.2 shows the circuit diagram which will allow you to construct a DIY programmer capable of programming 8K and 16K EPROMs. What we are aiming to do is to present an address and the byte to be programmed at the user port. For the byte to be programmed into the EPROM 21V (±0.5V) at 30mA is applied to pin 1 of the EPROM. This line is then pulsed low for 50msecs (±5msec).

The 21V voltage level is quite critical as a voltage less than 20.5V will result in the EPROM not being programmed; if it exceeds 22V then the EPROM will be damaged.

Programming the EPROM

During programming, the 3-pole toggle switch, S1, must be switched so that the 'not programming enable' line, NPGM, is brought into the circuit so that it connects to the CB2 line and also switches the 21V onto pin 1 of the EPROM already placed in the ZIF socket. The programming software presented in Program 11.1 can then be RUN.

The program now takes the address – in fact, its offset – into the EPROM. The first byte is at &0000, and presents each byte to the user port where it is clocked into the two address latches on the board. The data byte is then extracted from the Beeb's memory and presented to the data pins of the

```
  10 REM Program EPROM
  20 REM (c) Bruce Smith
  30 REM September 1984
  40 REM The BBC Micro ROM Book
  50 DIM code 170
  60 byte=&70
  70 page=&71
  80 address=&72
  90 osbyte=&FFF4
 100 osword=&FFF1
 110 oswrch=&FFEE
 120 !&70=0
 130 !&72=&3000
 140 PROCassemble
 150 MODE 7
 160 PRINTCHR$(141);CHR$(129);SPC(6);"E
PROM Programmer"
 170 PRINTCHR$(141);CHR$(129);SPC(6);"E
PROM Programmer"
 180 PRINTTAB(0,23);CHR$(130);"Press an
y key to begin programming";
 190 key=GET
 200 PRINTTAB(1,8);"Address of current
byte :&";
 210 CALL code
 220 END
 230 :
 240 DEF PROCassemble
 250 FOR pass=0 TO 2 STEP 2
 260 P%=code
 270 [              OPT pass
 280 .program_loop
 290              LDA #&97
 300              LDX #&6E
 310              LDY #0
 320              JSR osbyte
 330              :
 340              LDX #&62
 350              LDY #&FF
 360              JSR osbyte
 370              :
 380              LDX #&60
 390              LDY page
 400              JSR osbyte
 410              :
 420              LDX #&61
 430              LDY byte
 440              JSR osbyte
 450              :
 460              LDX #&6C
```

```
470              LDY #&CE
480              JSR osbyte
490              :
500              LDY #&CC
510              JSR osbyte
520              :
530              LDY #0
540              LDA (address).Y
550              TAY
560              :
570              LDA #&97
580              LDX #&60
590              JSR osbyte
600              :
610              LDX #&6C
620              LDY #&EC
630              JSR osbyte
640              :
650              JSR time
660              :
670              LDY #&97
680              LDX #&6C
690              LDY #&CC
700              JSR osbyte
710              :
720              INC address
730              BNE over
740              INC address+1
750 .over
760              :
770              JSR hexaddr
780              :
790              INC byte
800              BNE noinc
810              INC page
820 .noinc
830              :
840              LDA page
850              CMP #32
860              BNE program_loop
870              RTS
880              :
890 .time
900              LDA #2
910              LDX #clock MOD 256
920              LDY #clock DIV 256
930              JSR osword
940              :
950 .read
960              LDA #1
```

```
 970               LDX #&74
 980               LDY #0
 990               JSR osword
1000               LDA &74
1010               BNE read
1020               RTS
1030               :
1040 .clock
1050               EQUD &FFFFFFFB
1060               EQUB &FF
1070               :
1080 .hexaddr
1090               LDA #31
1100               JSR oswrch
1110               LDA #27
1120               JSR oswrch
1130               LDA #8
1140               JSR oswrch
1150               LDA address+1
1160               JSR hexout
1170               LDA address
1180 .hexout
1190               PHA
1200               LSR A
1210               LSR A
1220               LSR A
1230               LSR A
1240               JSR digit
1250               PLA
1260 .digit
1270               AND #15
1280               CMP #10
1290               BCC less
1300               ADC #6
1310 .less
1320               ADC #48
1330               JMP oswrch
1340 ]
1350 NEXT pass
1360 ENDPROC
```

Program 11.1. EPROM programmer.

EPROM, pins 11 to 19, except pin 14, and the NPGM line is then pulsed low for the required duration. This process is repeated for the entire 8 kbytes of data and, when completed, S1 should be switched back to disable the 21V connection.

The entire operational sequence in steps is therefore:

(a) Load program.

(b) Load data into memory from &3000.

(c) Ensure S1 is set to 'off' position.

(d) Place blank EPROM into ZIF socket.

(e) Switch S1 to 'on' or program position.

(f) RUN program.

(g) Switch S1 to 'off' position.

(h) Verify EPROM contents.

(i) Remove EPROM.

(j) Cover EPROM window with named label.

The last step is important because if the silicon wafer visible within the EPROM is exposed to sunlight its contents could be erased. Labelling is important – a shelf of EPROMs without a label to tell you what they are is infuriating – as I've proved!

Verifying or copying an EPROM

Program 11.2 will verify an EPROM's

```
 10 REM EPROM Verify Routine
 20 REM (c) Bruce Smith
 30 REM September 1984
 40 REM The BBC Micro ROM Book
 50 :
 60 MODE 7
 70 PRINT CHR$(129):CHR$(141);SPC(6):
 80 PRINT"EPROM Verifier"
 90 PRINT CHR$(129):CHR$(141);SPC(6):
100 PRINT"EPROM Verifier"
110 DIM code 200
120 byte=&70
130 page=&71
140 address=&72
150 check=&74
160 osbyte=&FFF4
170 osasci=&FFE3
180 !byte=0
190 !address=&3000
200 PROCverify
210 PRINT''CHR$(136);"Verifying EPROM"
220 CALL code
230 PRINT''"EPROM Checked"
240 END
250 :
260 DEF PROCverify
270 FOR pass=0 TO 2 STEP 2
280 P%=code
290 [              OPT pass
300 .verify
```

```
310                 LDA #&97
320                 LDX #&6E
330                 LDY #0
340                 JSR osbyte
350             :
360                 LDX #&62
370                 LDY #&FF
380                 JSR osbyte
390             :
400                 LDX #&60
410                 LDY page
420                 JSR osbyte
430             :
440                 LDX #&61
450                 LDY byte
460                 JSR osbyte
470             :
480                 LDX #&6C
490                 LDY #&CE
500                 JSR osbyte
510             :
520                 LDY #&CC
530                 JSR osbyte
540             :
550                 LDX #&62
560                 LDY #0
570                 JSR osbyte
580             :
590                 LDX #&6C
600                 LDY #&EC
610                 JSR osbyte
620             :
630                 LDA #&96
640                 LDX #&60
650                 JSR osbyte
660                 STY check
670             :
680                 LDA #&97
690                 LDX #&6C
700                 LDY #&CC
710                 JSR osbyte
720             :
730                 LDY #0
740                 LDA (address),Y
750                 CMP check
760                 BNE error
770             :
780 .update
790                 INC address
800                 BNE over
810                 INC address+1
```

```
 820 .over
 830              INC byte
 840              BNE leap
 850              INC page
 860 .leap
 870              LDA page
 880              CMP #32
 890              BNE verify
 900              RTS
 910              :
 920 .error
 930              PHA
 940              LDY #&FF
 950 .printerror
 960              INY
 970              LDA ascii,Y
 980              JSR osasci
 990              BNE printerror
1000              JSR hexaddr
1010              JSR space
1020              PLA
1030              JSR hexout
1040              JSR space
1050              LDA check
1060              JSR hexout
1070              JMP update
1080              :
1090 .hexaddr
1100              LDA address+1
1110              JSR hexout
1120              LDA address
1130 .hexout
1140              PHA
1150              LSR A
1160              LSR A
1170              LSR A
1180              LSR A
1190              JSR digit
1200              PLA
1210 .digit
1220              AND #15
1230              CMP #10
1240              BCC less
1250              ADC #6
1260 .less
1270              ADC #48
1280              JMP osasci
1290              :
1300 .space
1310              LDA #&20
1320              JSR osasci
```

```
1330                  LDA #ASC("&")
1340                  JMP osasci
1350                  :
1360 .ascii
1370                  EQUB 13
1380                  EQUS "Verify error at :&"
1390                  EQUB 0
1400 ]
1410 NEXT
1420 ENDPROC
```

Program 11.2 EPROM verifier.

contents against the 8K of data stored in memory from &3000 onwards. Program 11.3 will copy the contents of an EPROM in the ZIF socket into the Beeb's memory from &3000 onwards.

Switch S1 should be in the 'off', NOE (not output enable position) to allow each byte of data to be read from the EPROM and placed in the user port. Depending on the program in use, the byte will then be compared with the one in memory or poked into memory.

```
  10 REM EPROM Copier
  20 REM (c) Bruce Smith
  30 REM September 1984
  40 REM The BBC micro ROM Book
  50 :
  60 DIM code 200
  70 byte=&70
  80 page=&71
  90 address=&72
 100 osbyte=&FFF4
 110 oswrch=&FFEE
 120 !byte=0
 130 !address=&3000
 140 MODE 7
 150 PRINTCHR$(141);(CHR$129);SPC(9);
 160 PRINT"EPROM Copier"
 170 PRINTCHR$(141);(CHR$129);SPC(9);
 180 PRINT"EPROM Copier"
 190 PRINTTAB(1,10);"Copying byte to :&
 ";
 200 PROCcopy
 210 CALL code
 220 PRINT''''" 8192 bytes copied"
 230 END
 240 DEF PROCcopy
 250 FOR PASS=0 TO 2 STEP 2
 260 P%=code
 270 [                OPT PASS
 280 .copy
```

```
290             LDA #&97
300             LDX #&6E
310             LDY #0
320             JSR osbyte
330             :
340             LDX #&62
350             LDY #&FF
360             JSR osbyte
370             :
380             LDX #&60
390             LDY page
400             JSR osbyte
410             :
420             LDX #&61
430             LDY byte
440             JSR osbyte
450             :
460             LDX #&6C
470             LDY #&CE
480             JSR osbyte
490             :
500             LDY #&CC
510             JSR osbyte
520             :
530             LDX #&62
540             LDY #0
550             JSR osbyte
560             :
570             LDX #&6C
580             LDY #&EC
590             JSR osbyte
600             :
610             LDA #&96
620             LDX #&60
630             JSR osbyte
640             TYA
650             LDY #0
660             STA (address),Y
670             :
680             LDA #&97
690             LDX #&6C
700             LDY #&CC
710             JSR osbyte
720             :
730             INC address
740             BNE over
750             INC address+1
760 .over
770             :
780             JSR hexaddr
```

```
 790                :
 800                INC byte
 810                BNE leap
 820                INC page
 830 .leap
 840                :
 850                LDA page
 860                CMP #32
 870                BNE copy
 880                RTS
 890                :
 900                :
 910 .hexaddr
 920                LDA #31
 930                JSR oswrch
 940                LDA #19
 950                JSR oswrch
 960                LDA #10
 970                JSR oswrch
 980                LDA address+1
 990                JSR hexout
1000                LDA address
1010 .hexout
1020                PHA
1030                LSR A
1040                LSR A
1050                LSR A
1060                LSR A
1070                JSR digit
1080                PLA
1090 .digit
1100                AND #15
1110                CMP #10
1120                BCC less
1130                ADC #6
1140 .less
1150                ADC #48
1160                JMP oswrch
1170                :
1180 ]
1190 NEXT
1200 ENDPROC
```

Program 11.3. EPROM copier.

The entire sequence for verifying or copying an EPROM is therefore:

(a) Load appropriate program.
(b) If verifying, ensure data present in memory from &3000.
(c) Ensure S1 is in 'off' position.

(d) Insert appropriate EPROM into socket.

(e) RUN program.

(f) If copying EPROM save data.

(g) If verifying and an error occurs, reprogram new EPROM.

Angry Violet

Damn, you've just verified your EPROM and there's an error in it – what do you do? It's pretty unusual for a verify error to occur and once your programmer is running correctly it should never really occur. There are a number of possible reasons – the most obvious one is that there is a loose connection somewhere so go around all the mechanical connections as these are most susceptible. Perhaps one of the solder joints on the EPROM programmer board has become damaged? Or the EPROM was not correctly placed in the ZIF socket? It's also worth checking that the data being verified in the Beeb has not been corrupted in some way. Finally, is your program correct?

If you need to redo your EPROM or perhaps you have a couple of 'old' ones lying around that contain programs you want to get rid of, what do you do? Basically, the EPROM must be erased by subjecting it to ultra-violet radiation at a wavelength of 275.8nm for about 20 minutes. UV radiation can be dangerous, so treat it with the utmost respect as it can cause blindness.

If you want to erase an EPROM you will need to have access to an EPROM eraser. These can be bought for twenty pounds or so, and do the job well. Just take care!

Chapter Twelve
BASIC Toolkits

BASIC Toolkits are essentially service ROMs that can provide two functions. First, they provide suitable BASIC program debugging aids generally termed 'utilities', and second, they enhance the already versatile BBC BASIC by providing extra commands. Some BASIC toolkits provide both of these features while others are just debugging aids; it is rare to find an enhancement ROM only.

Before purchasing a BASIC toolkit it is worth making a list of the sort of things you wish to do. Armed with this list, the best toolkit for your needs can be selected and purchased. It may be that you cannot find all you need in a single toolkit so that two may be needed to meet all your requirements. This would work out to be rather expensive, as most toolkits cost over £20. In this instance it would be worth purchasing the one containing the more complex coding and perhaps writing your own software to provide the less complex utilities.

To enable you to make your choice of ROM, what follows is a command by command blow of each of the toolkits covered in this chapter, with an overview of its contents.

ADDCOMM

If value for money is what you are after then the ADDCOMM ROM from Vine Micros might well come out on top of your list. Forty commands are implemented, using the 'Mistake' BRK trapping approach outlined in Chapter 8. Thus commands need not be prefixed by an operating system asterisk, or limited to a single line or last statement on a line. A drawback of this method of command detection is that it can lead to incorrect error messages being generated occasionally.

The Toolkit is organised into three sections. These are

(a) Toolkit commands
(b) Enhanced graphics
(c) LOGO graphics

so the toolkit is both a utility and enhancement ROM. When ADDCOMM is 'on' it raises the value of PAGE by 256 bytes.

The command details are as follows:

ADDCOMM: Turns ADDCOMM off.

ADVANCE: Used to advance the LOGO cursor in current direction.

ANGLE: Sets the direction of the LOGO cursor.

CFILL: Defines colour grid for use by FILL.

CHAR: User-definable character designer.

CIRCLE: Draws a circle of any radius at an x,y co-ordinate. Extra parameters may be included to draw part circles or arcs.

COMPACT: Removes all excess spaces, and REMs from a program, constructing multi-statement lines where possible. The start and end lines for compaction may be specified.

ELLIPSE: Will draw an ellipse of any length axes at x,y co-ordinates specified. Part ellipses may be drawn.

FILL: Fills in colour defined by CFILL from x,y co-ordinate specified to a boundary.

FIND: Searches a program for a specified string of characters. Start and end lines may be specified.

FKEYS: Displays any function key definitions present.

GOODPROG: Mends a 'Bad Program' to make it listable.

GREPL: A global search and replace routine, that will replace all occurrences of a string with another.

KILLREM: Deletes all REMs within all or part of a program.

LCIRCLE: Draws a circle or part circle around current LOGO cursor position.

LELLIPSE: Draws an ellipse or part of an ellipse around the current LOGO cursor position.

LGOTO: Performs a GOTO to the specified label.

LLIST: Lists a line, can be used from within a program.

LMOVE: Moves the LOGO cursor to the specified co-ordinates.

LPOS: Returns the current position of the LOGO cursor.

LVAR: Lists some or all of variables currently in memory.

MEM: Lists program length, reserved memory and memory space remaining in hexadecimal and decimal bytes.

OPT: Used to set a variety of parameters for use with ADDCOMM.

PEN: Selects the PLOT code for use when drawing with the LOGO cursor.

POPFOR: Deletes current FOR...NEXT loop.

POPGOS: Deletes current subroutine return address.

POPREP: Deletes current REPEAT...UNTIL loop reference.

ROTATE: Rotates all current graphics output by specified angle about specified point.

SCALE: Sets screen scaling.

SDRAW: Uses current SCALE to DRAW with.

SETWIN: Allows up to seven multiple windows to be defined.
SMOVE: Uses current SCALE to MOVE to position specified.
SORT: Sorts all or part of a string array into alphabetical order.
SPLOT: PLOT to current SCALE co-ordinates.
SREPL: Selective search and replace facility allowing specified characters to be selectively replaced by another string of characters within all or part of a program.
TRANS: Translates scaled screen by vector displacement.
TURN: Turns LOGO cursor in stated direction.
UNSCALE: Returns screen to normal co-ordinate system scaling.
VERIFY: Verifies program file with program in memory – BASIC or machine code.
WIN: Selects specified user-defined window.

The ADDCOMM manual is a comprehensive 72-page, spiral-bound affair and includes several program demonstrations of its facilities.

CARETAKER

The Caretaker ROM from Computer Concepts is a service ROM placing eighteen extra commands at your fingertips. All the commands are concerned with programming and debugging and include a useful Electron emulator (!) which allows the programmer to enter commands with a single dual keystroke. For example, pressing the TAB key and A together will enter the command AUTO into the keyboard buffer.

Prefixing any Caretaker command with C allows ROM-clashing commands to be identified as Caretaker-specific by the utility ROM. All commands are implemented as operating system commands. The command details are as follows;

*CURSOR (ON/OFF): Enables or disables the flashing text cursor.
*EXCHANGE: Provides a global search and replacement facility for editing BASIC programs. It may be global or selective and includes a special wildcard feature.
*EXPAND: Displays a program in a specially formatted form, ensuring one command per line.
*INSERT: Allows BASIC routines or procedures on tape or disc to be loaded into an already present BASIC program.
*KEYLOAD: Loads previously saved function key definitions into the function key buffer.
*KEYSAVE: Saves the function key definitions to tape or disc.
*LVAR: Lists all program variables, functions and procedures. The command may be used to list selectively a certain variable or procedure as required.

```
*HELP CARETAKER

CARETAKER 1.00
    CURSOR (ON/OFF)
    EXCHANGE <old> <new> G/S (<length>)
    EXPAND (<start>) (<end>)
    INSERT <fsp> (<lineno>)
    KEYLOAD (<fsp>)
    KEYSAVE (<fsp>)
    LVAR (F)(I)(S)(A)(P)
    MOVE <address>
    MERGE <fsp> (<fsp>)...
    NORMALKEY
    NOTAB
    PARTSAVE <fsp> (<start>) (<end>)
    RENUMBER (<1st> <inc> <start> <end>)
    RETRIEVE (<bytes>)
    SINGLEKEY
    SQUASH (S)(R)(M)
    STATUS
    TABSTOPS (<columns...>)

OS 1.20
>
```

(a)

(b)

Fig. 12.1. (a) Caretaker help sheet (b) Caretaker ROM and manual.

MERGE: Merges a BASIC program on tape or disc with one already present in memory.

MOVE: Will move a BASIC program to a new PAGE setting.

NORMALKEY: Turns off the single key command entry facility.

NOTAB: Turns the TABSTOPS function off.

PARTSAVE: Saves the specified lines in a BASIC program to tape or disc.

RENUMBER: Renumbers a specific part of a BASIC program, moving the renumbered section as required.

RETRIEVE: Restores a 'Bad program'.

SINGLEKEY: Turns the single key command entry facility on.

SQUASH: Compacts a program to its smallest possible components. May be used to remove selectively REMs and spaces and create multi-statement lines.

STATUS: Displays values currently assigned to PAGE, TOP, LOMEM, HIMEM, VARTOP, together with memory remaining and current length of program.

TABSTOPS: Allows TAB key to be used as originally designed on a typewriter – to TAB cursor x columns across the screen.

The Caretaker manual is somewhat light, but its thirty spiral bound pages are professionally produced.

TOOLKIT

TOOLKIT is an 8K utilities EPROM by Beebug. Eighteen commands are provided, though one of these, *UTIL, provides a further eight. The most pleasing aspect of TOOLKIT is its line editor that allows you to move through programs, in any direction, for editing with ease. The editor can also be switched on to highlight run time errors, making the debugging process that much easier. All commands may be prefixed with a B to identify them as a TOOLKIT command if a ROM command clash does occur.

The command details are as follows:

CHECK: Verifies the specified file, on disc or cassette, with that in memory. The file may be BASIC or machine code as the comparison is byte by byte.

CLEAR: This acts in a similar manner to BASIC's CLEAR command but also includes the system integer variables.

EDIT: Enters screen editor.

FREE: Displays values of PAGE, LOMEM, TOP and HIMEM in addition to giving program size and memory free details.

MEMORY: Produces a hex and ASCII dump of memory.

MERGE: Merges a named program file on tape or disc with a program already present in memory.

MOVE: Relocates a BASIC program elsewhere in memory.

NEW: Same as BASIC's NEW but may be used from within a program (!).

OLD: Same as BASIC's OLD but may be used from within a program.

ON: Enables TOOLKIT's enhanced error-handling capabilities.

ONF: As *ON but sets the values of the first two function keys as follows:

f0 *BEDIT
f1 *BUTIL

The B signifies the TOOLKIT command.

OFF: Cancels the *ON command.

PACK: Compacts a BASIC program. *PACK will remove all spaces, REMs and comments. *PACK S will remove just spaces; *PACK R is as *PACK but will also remove assembler comments.

RECOVER: Restores a 'Bad program'.

RENUMBER: Allows part or all of a program to be renumbered as required.

REPORT: Is the equivalent of the BASIC line, *REPORT:PRINT" Error at line ";ERL.*

SCREEN: Saves current screen memory to a named file.

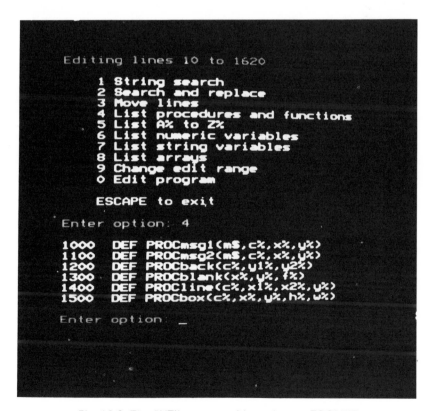

Fig. 12.2. The *UTIL command in action on TOOLKIT.

UTIL: Enters utility editor, provides a menu for the following commands to be executed, which may also be executed using the following from BASIC itself.

UTIL 1: Searches and displays line containing named string. Wildcards may be used.

UTIL 2: Searches and replaces first named string with second named string, in a BASIC program.

UTIL 3: Moves specified program lines to another part of the program.

UTIL 4: Lists all DEF PROCs and DEF FNs within a program.

UTIL 5: Lists the current values assigned to integer variables A% to Z% in decimal and hexadecimal.

UTIL 6: Lists all other numeric variables in decimal and hexadecimal.

UTIL 7: Lists all string variables and the strings currently assigned to them.

UTIL 8: Lists all currently defined arrays, with their dimensions.

UTIL 9: Changes line numbers of the edit range.

The commands *UTIL 5, 6, 7, and 8, will only work correctly after a program has been run. This is because they are extracted from above TOP rather than from the program itself as the latter would only provide initially assigned values.

U TOOLS

U TOOLS by Intersoft is a utility ROM providing twenty-six extra commands to the Beeb's vocabulary. All commands may be abbreviated and may be in either upper- or lower-case. The U TOOLS command details are described below:

CVAR: Clears the BASIC integer variables, A% to Z%, to zero and resets the default value of @%.

CRUNCH: Compacts a BASIC program to its smallest form by using multi-statement lines.

DECOM: Removes all spaces, REMs, blank lines and assembler comments from a program.

DEREM: Removes all REM statements from a BASIC program.

DESPC: Removes all redundant spaces from within a program.

EXPAND: Opens up a space in the line numbering of a program so that extra lines may be entered at a specific point.

FIND: Lists all the lines within a program that contain a specified string.

HEXDUMP: Prints a hex and ASCII dump of memory from a start to end address.

HVAR: Lists variables in hexadecimal format.

HVAR%: Lists the resident integer variables in hexadecimal format.

KEYS: Lists the current function key assignments.

LOCK: Locks a machine code program to make it 'unreadable' by others.

LSTERR: Prints out erroneous line at all future errors.

LSTERROFF: Turns above facility off.

LVAR: Lists the values assigned to all variables, string variables and the strings assigned to them and arrays and their predefined dimensions. All variable values are in decimal.

LVAR%: Lists the values assigned to the resident integer variables in decimal.

MEMLOCS: Displays all current program information. Includes values of TOP, PAGE, HIMEM, LOMEM, LISTO, WIDTH, *FX4, *FX9, *FX10, *FX11, *FX12, plus memory remaining, the size of the current program and the memory storage used by variables.

MERGE: Merges a program file with a program already present in memory.

PDUMP: Dumps the graphics screen contents to a connected printer (Epson-compatible).

REMOVE: A high-speed DELETE.

REPAIR: Repairs a 'Bad Program'.

REPLACE: Finds and replaces occurrences of a specified string or command with a special string.

RESTART: Resets the whole of user RAM from &400 upwards.

SHIFT: Relocates a BASIC program to a new PAGE setting.

SPREAD: Formats a listing, making it easier to read after a *CRUNCH has been performed on it.

UNLOCK: Complements *LOCK by unlocking a previously *LOCKed file.

BASIC Extensions

This ROM by the established software house, Micro Power, adds two types of command to the BBC Micro, and is another value for money ROM. The first is a series of 'direct' utilities which are aids to program writing and debugging. The second, and probably most interesting, consists of a series of additional statements that can be used within a BASIC program.

The Extensions ROM uses one page of private workspace, thus raising PAGE by this amount, but it may be stopped from initialising itself by pressing A-BREAK.

As the program statements added are rather original, these are looked at first. In all there are twenty-three, and these are error-trapped so the normal OS asterisk is not required for them to be interpreted. The commands are also tokenised, though the tokens require two bytes.

The Extensions ROM also allows procedures to be called by name only. Thus a PROC called PROCtester may be called directly by the pseudo command 'tester'.

Four new loop structures are included:

WHILE...ENDWHILE: This is similar to the REPEAT...UNTIL loop except that it executes all the instructions it encloses WHILE the condition it is testing remains true. Thus,

```
WHILE X%<>0
  PRINT X%
  INPUT X%
ENDWHILE
```

will continue to print the value of X% while X% is not equal to 0. Up to 31 levels may be nested.

CASE...WHEN...OTHERWISE...ENDCASE: This takes the variable defined in CASE and applies it to the conditionals in the WHEN statements. When the condition is found to be true the instructions after it are executed. If every WHEN is false then the OTHERWISE instructions will be executed if present.

```
CASE x%
  WHEN 2
    A%=A%+2
  WHEN 4
    A%=A%+4
  OTHERWISE
    A%=A%+10
ENDCASE
```

Up to 20 levels may be nested, and PROCs may be used as part of a WHEN, using only its name, i.e. convert instead of PROCconvert.

LOOP...EXITIF...(THEN)...ENDEXIT...ENDLOOP...: LOOP and ENDLOOP set up an indefinite loop. When EXITIF is encountered, the conditional after it is evaluated and, if true, the commands after it are executed until the ENDEXIT is reached. If the conditional after this statement is evaluated as true the program flow will continue at the instruction after the ENDLOOP statement thereby leaving the loop itself. Otherwise the loop will simply continue.

FIF...(THEN)...(ELSEIF)...ENDIF: This is a multiple line version of the normal IF...THEN...ELSE structure that may be nested to any depth. Both THEN and ELSEIF are optional.

The remaining program statements are as follows:

FPOP: Removes the last FOR...NEXT loop from the stack.

GPOP: Removes the last RETURN address from the stack.

KILL: Turns the BASIC Extensions ROM off.

MEMSHIFT: Takes an area of memory and transfers it to another specified address.

ORIGIN: Re-positions the graphics origin as VDU 29.

SETTEXT: Defines a text window as VDU 28.

SETCOLOUR: Sets physical colour displayed for each logical colour as VDU19.

SETGRAPHIC: Defines a graphics window as VDU 24.

LPRINT: Acts like print but output is to a printer.

RUN: As BASIC's RUN but will clear the Extensions stack.

The direct mode utilities are described below:

BTOD: Converts a binary number into decimal.

COMPACT: Removes all surplus spaces, REMs and comments from within a BASIC program.

CONT: This attempts to restart running a program, from where execution was terminated.

FIND: Will search for every occurrence of a specified string, listing the line where it occurs. It will also work on all tokens. Wildcards are permitted keywords.

CHANGE: Will search and replace all occurrences of a specified string by another, including all tokenised keywords. Wildcards are permitted.

DTOB: Converts a 32-bit decimal number, including an expression, into binary.

DUMP: Will print out the decimal values of all dynamic variables. Arrays will have only the zeroth element printed. Post-fixing the command with a title (DUMP~) will produce output in hexadecimal.

DUMP %: As for DUMP but outputs decimal (or hexadecimal) values of resident integer variables.

JOIN: Adds a specified program file onto the end of a BASIC program already in memory.

LISTO: Additional LISTO options have been added, printing extra spaces to handle the new loop structures.

MERGE: Merges a specified file with a BASIC program already in memory, positioning lines correctly within the program.

SECURE: Allows you to add a password to gain access to your BBC Micro.

SHIFT: Allows parts of programs to be 'moved' around. Source lines are left intact.

STATUS: Displays amount of current memory space.

VERIFY: Checks that the BASIC program on tape or disc is the same as that in memory.

VIEW: Lists the specified BASIC program directly from the filing system without affecting memory.

WILDCARD: Allows the wildcard character used in FIND and CHANGE to be defined. The default character is '?'.

SLEUTH

SLEUTH is a very sophisticated BASIC debugging tool by Beebug. If you are familiar with machine code monitors then it is true to say that SLEUTH is a BASIC Monitor!

A dual screen approach is used that allows you to view on-screen just what your program is doing – vital if it is a graphics-orientated program – while a single TAB keypress will return you to the SLEUTH control screen.

Each program line may be stepped through, command by command, and stopped at any point. Variables used by the program may be examined at this point and altered as required.

Breakpoints may be defined – thus the program can be set to stop at a predefined point or even when a variable assignment is attained.

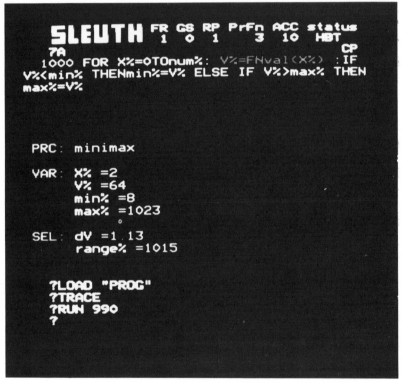

Fig. 12.3. Beebug's SLEUTH.

Chapter Thirteen
Extra, Extra!

Monitoring machine code

If you take your assembler programming seriously then a machine code monitor is, quite simply, an absolute must. It will allow you to debug a machine code program, and edit and inspect the data it invokes in a variety of ways. No longer need you spend hours bent over the keyboard looking for a mistake in the logic of your program, or more often than not the typing error that you are continually overlooking! Virtually without exception, machine code monitors are implemented as language ROMs. The vocabulary of the monitor's language will vary according to the sophistication of the monitor itself, but usually it will simply consist of a dialect of letters – each key pressed invoking a particular process.

Like learning any language (parlez vous francais?) the hard part is starting. Once you understand the fundamentals behind a language's construction and its overall constraints you are well on your way. Using it frequently and regularly will improve your vocabulary until you are quite fluent.

Machine code monitors are not user-friendly so if you make a mistake don't expect the polite banter of BASIC – a question mark and a single word is generally more usual – but we 'pokeyites' can withstand the pressure of it all!

Mean machine

Choosing a machine code monitor to suit your own needs is, to say the least, difficult. The overall standard of those produced for the BBC Micro is extremely high, and with one or two exceptions, you would not be disappointed with any of them. Most offer the same facilities, which is understandable as there are only certain things one can do when monitoring machine code. However, some do differ so if you are looking for a particular function then it is worth shopping around and examining each in turn. For example, if you are keen on machine code graphics, then a machine code monitor that allows the use of dual screens is essential to enable you to examine the graphic detail and then switch to the monitor's 'screen' to see the overall state of play.

A description of several machine code monitors would be a difficult task and would not do any of them credit. If you think I'm taking the easy way out then you're quite right, but I would challenge you to describe a language in a few hundred words or so – go on, try it with BASIC! What I have done below, therefore, is to list the various *HELP sheets for each monitor. This will give an indication of the facilities available on each. I have added comments where the *HELP sheet is a little vague: this should provide you with a general view of each of the monitor's cover and allow you to investigate ones that catch your eye further.

ADE

ADE by System Software is a 16K EPROM and comes supplied with demo disc and a hefty (no page numbers – sections only) spiral-bound manual.

```
>*HELP ADE

ADE 1.00
  ADE
  ASM <sfsp> <ofsp>
  BRK
  CTRLF
  ED (<fsp>)
  EDIT (<fsp>)
  FX100,<lo>,<hi>
  LST
  MODE <n>
  NOBRK
  NOCTRLF
  SPY
```

Fig. 13.1. The ADE help sheet.

The ADE chip contains a full word processing editor, the SPY series 1 debugger and a full 6502 macro assembler. Figure 13.1 shows the *HELP sheet.

ADE selects command level; no parameters are required by any command.
ASM selects the macro assembler.
BRK enables breakpoints.
CTRLF invokes single key entry into the SPY debugger.
EDIT initialises the word processor.
LST enters the disassembler.
MODE allows the screen mode to be defined or changed within ADE.
NOBRK reverses *BRK.

*NOCTRLF reverses *CTRLF.
*SPY enters the debugging monitor.

This description does not really do the ADE monitor credit. It is very sophisticated and the three main areas within it contain a whole host of sub-commands. For example, the macro assembler invoked by *ASM contains no less than 29 extra pseudo opcodes while the SPY debugging monitor has over 30 selections in command mode.

DEBUG

DEBUG is an 8K EPROM that will work in any screen mode. Although DEBUG is primarily a language ROM its service interpreter also allows its commands to be executed as such so that each is available from the 'outside'. Figure 13.2 shows the *HELP sheet.

```
>*HELP DEBUG

DEBUG 1.00

   * <OSCLI>
   : <numb> , <arg>
   ; <numb> (<arg>)
   B (<numb>) (<numb>)
   C (S O L) <numb> <numb> <numb>
   D (<numb>) (, <numb>)
   E
   F <numb> <numb> <arg>
   G (<numb>)
   H (S O L) <numb> <numb> <arg>
   J (<numb>)
   M (<numb>) (, <numb>)
   O <numb> <arg>
   P (D H B) <arg>
   R
   S <arg>
   T <numb> <numb> <numb>
   V <arg>
   W (<numb>) (<numb>)^
```

Fig. 13.2. The DEBUG help sheet.

To help you unravel the meaning of each letter a description of each is as follows:

*   pass command to OSCLI.
:   alter memory.
;   alter contents of processor registers.
B   set up to eight breakpoints.

C compare memory blocks.
D disassemble memory.
E return last error message and its number.
F fill memory with specified value.
G execute machine code.
H search memory for specified bytes.
J execute subroutine.
M hex and ASCII memory dump.
O perform specified OSWORD call.
P print argument in hex, binary or decimal.
R display processor registers.
S select a sideways ROM on which to operate.
T transfer data between memory or ROMs.
V perform the VDU OSWRCH function.
W single step through machine code.

The use of S is limited as you cannot (officially) gain access to the DEBUG ROM itself!
DEBUG will work with a second processor.

EXMON I

EXMON by Beebug is one of the more friendly machine code monitors – possibly because it does attempt to use a bit of colour here and there. It is limited to use in MODE 7, however.

The HELP menu from within EXMON is extremely helpful and completely self-explanatory – as it should be – and is shown in Fig. 13.3.

```
General Commands:   Debugging Commands:
_____ _____    _____ _____
L List memory       @  Set PC
D Disassemble       A  Set accumulator
K Disassemble+save  X  Set X register
N Assemble          Y  Set Y register
E Edit (ESC ends,   P  Set PSW
  space goes back)  S  Set stack pointer
" ASCII to memory   GO Execute program
FS/FB Find string      (space) Simulate
M Move block        /  Step on one level
V Verify blocks     Z  Trace
I Fill              B  Set breakpoint
T Change panel      U  Delete breakpoint
C Calculate         W  Delete all
OB/OW Osbyte/word   J  JSR
! Change paged ROM  _____
R Relocate program  ?  Help summary
H Print             Q  Quit EXMON
```

Fig. 13.3. The EXMON help sheet.

The user-definable keys may be used to program frequently used commands so that they are available for use at a single keystroke. The C calculate command uses BASIC's expression evaluator so that fully fledged arithmetic expression can be evaluated from within EXMON. The result is displayed in hexadecimal and decimal. The program relocation command, R, will move a machine code program and attempt to adjust all addresses within it to match its new location.

EXMON II

The very latest version of EXMON is EXMON II. This is similar to the original but has many enhancements including a dual screen facility to enable graphics programs to be run as you toggle between the graphics screen and the EXMON control screen.

The breakpoint option has been improved to handle up to ten breakpoints which may be conditional and even set in ROM. A total of sixty commands are present in EXMON II.

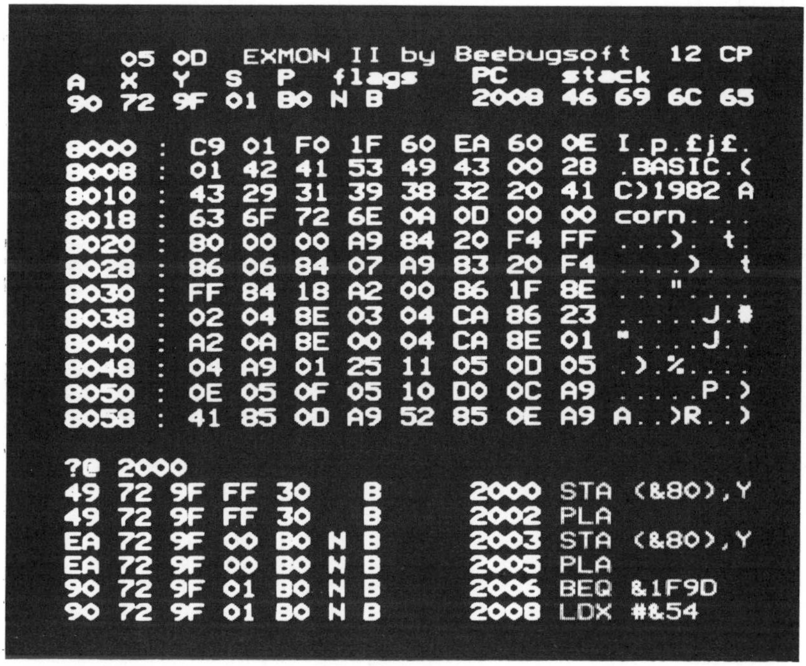

Fig. 13.4. EXMON II in action.

Gremlin

Gremlin is an 8K monitor by Computer Concepts. Figure 13.6 shows the Gremlin help sheet.

The *IND* command allows the user to follow through vectors and linked lists.

Fig. 13.5. Gremlin machine language monitor.

```
GREMLIN 1.21
  M <addr> :Memory ptr
  + <expr>
  - <expr>
  IND
  J <addr> :Jump
  LB, SB   :List, Set Breakpoints
  .var=<expr> :Set variable
  LVAR, CLEAR :List, clear all vars
  MODE <expr> :Screen Mode
  P <data> :Put
  F <data> :Find
  where <data>=byte,word;"string",ASM
  PRINT<expr>
  CALL <addr>
  D <strt> <end> (S)(F"file"<heading>)
  IM <first> <last> <amount>
  SWITCHES: HX HN SE AO JE DR PF
  SYSTEM VARIABLES (preceded by S)
    registers A X Y P S PC
    general ROM M VL,VH DL,DH
    breakpoints B0 .. B7

OS 1.20
```

Fig. 13.6. The Gremlin help sheet.

IM is an intelligent move routine that will not allow the data which is to be moved to be overwritten.

D is disassembly, and output may be to a tape or disc file which may later be reloaded to form an assembler listing.

SWITCHES allow certain conditions to be toggled so that events are allowed to occur or not.

Gremlin includes a two-pass assembler and will work in any screen mode. Its output may be redirected so machine code graphics may be monitored.

The Gremlin manual is 32 pages long and spiral-bound.

Interpreter

This is an 8K EPROM from MIRRA Systems and is implemented as both a language and service ROM.

```
>*HELPINT
  INTERPRETER
  KEYLOCK
  VARLIST
  UDK
  UDKS
  UDKR
  UDKA
  UDKC
  UDKP
  INROM
  FRITZ
  HELPINT
```

Fig. 13.7. The Interpreter help sheet.

The *HELP menu is shown in Fig. 13.7, with details of each command as follows:

INTERPRETER selects the machine code interpreter.
KEYLOCK locks the computer's keyboard.
VARLIST lists active variables, PROCs and FNs.
UDK sets up user-defined key definitions.
UDKS saves user-defined key definitions.
UDKR restores user-defined key definitions.
UDKA sets &A00 to &AFF for UDK.
UDKC sets &C00 to &CFF for UDK storage.
UDKP prints user-defined key functions.
INROM downloads sideways ROM into memory.
FRITZ sets resident integer to zero.

When the machine code interpreter is entered, the standard range of commands are available. Full use of colour is made throughout which is eye-pleasing.

Utility ROMs

There are numerous sideways ROMs available to provide specific utilities for a particular area of Beeb use. These are all implemented as service ROMs and the ones covered here are, (a) Graphics Extension ROM; (b) Printmaster; (c) Disc Doctor; (d) MUROM; (e) HELP ROM.

Graphics Extension ROM
This is produced by Computer Concepts and is, surprisingly enough, the only ROM I know that has been written to enhance the graphics capabilities of the Beeb. The graphics extension is divided into three areas of operation, sprite graphics, turtle graphics, and general graphics, Details of the commands associated with each area of operation now follow:

Sprite graphics
RESERVE reserves a specified area of memory for sprite data.
DATA displays details of each sprite.
DESIGN places a grid onto the screen to allow sprites to be designed using defined keys.
FILM allows sprite animation sequences to be constructed.
ALTER is used to edit sprites.
RESET deletes specified sprites.
PUT allows sprites of films to be saved.

Fig. 13.8. The Graphics Extension ROM.

GET loads sprite or film definitions previously *PUT.

IN places a predefined sprite or film on screen.

OUT removes sprite or film frame from screen.

IMAGE allows a copy of a sprite to be made.

Turtle graphics

TURTLE defines shape, size and colour of graphics turtle.

POS positions turtle on screen at specified position and angle.

PENUP lifts drawing pen off paper.

PENDOWN places drawing pen down on paper.

LEFT rotates turtle left by specified number of degrees.

RIGHT rotates turtle right by specified number of degrees.

FORWARD moves turtle forward specified distance.

BACKWARD moves turtle backwards specified distance.

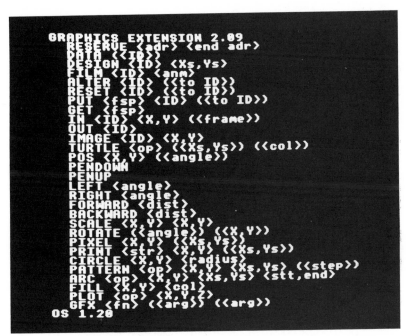

Fig. 13.9. Graphics Extension help sheet.

General graphics

SCALE allows user to define screen co-ordinate size.

ROTATE will rotate all future screen addressing commands by a specified angle around specified co-ordinates.

PIXEL plots multi-sized pixels.

PRINT allows printing of multi-sized, multi-coloured and multi-patterned characters on screen.

CIRCLE draws a circle of a specified radius.

PATTERN allows patterns to be drawn on the screen as specified in arguments.

ARC draws an arc specified in arguments onto the screen.

FILL is used to fill any shape on the screen in a specified colour.

PLOT is like PLOT but operates in three dimensions, X, Y and Z.

GFX is similar to *DATA but returns information in the resident integer variables.

MODE 8 is an extra screen MODE. It is a 16-colour mode but uses only 10K of memory. Text resolution is 10 by 32 characters, and 80 by 256 graphics.

The Graphics Extension ROM can be turned off using *FX240, 128 and re-enabled with *FX 240.

Printmaster

As its names suggests, this is a printer toolkit ROM. Two versions are available from Computer Concepts for either the Epson or Star printers. The commands available for the Epson version are as follows:

DEFINE allows user-definable characters to be designed or edited.

FDUMP sends an ASCII or SPOOL file to the printer while allowing the user to continue working with the Beeb.

FONT changes printer font to an international character set.

GDUMP dumps any graphics mode including MODE 7 to the printer. The dump can be multi-tone or two-tone, true or inverse.

```
PRINTMASTER (Epson) 1.02
  DEFINE <chr>
  FDUMP ((fsp))
  FONT <country>
  GDUMP ((or,op)) ((X,Y)) ((gap))
  GPRINT <str> <X,Y> ((or,op)) ((gap))
  INITIALISE
  ITALIC ((on/off))
  LINCH <lines per inch>
  LINESPACE ((a)) ((/b inches))
  MARGIN ((left)) ((right/+width))
  PAGELEN ((inches/+lines)) ((skip))
  PCODE <codes/$ASCII>
  PROPORTION ((on/off))
  STYLE <str>
  TAB <columns ..>
  TDUMP ((udc width))
  TEXT ((width)) ((shade)) ((height))
  TPRINT <str> <chr> ((X,Y)) ((or,op))
  ULOAD <fsp>
  UNDERLINE ((on/off))
  USAVE <fsp>
  WINDOW
  WVALS
OS 1.20
```

Fig. 13.10. Printmaster help sheet.

GPRINT prints multi-sized characters in up to eight orientations on the printer.

INITIALISE resets printer to default settings.

ITALIC allows italic printing to be switched ON and OFF.

LINCH sets number of lines per inch.

LINESPACE sets linespacing on printer.

MARGIN allows printer's left- and right-hand margins to be defined.

PAGELEN sets printer's page length and number of lines to be skipped at its end.

PCODE sends control codes to printer.

PROPORTION turns proportional printing ON and OFF.

STYLE selects printing style, i.e. enlarged, condensed, emphasised, etc.

TAB selects printer TAB positions.

TDUMP copies text in text window, or whole screen otherwise, to printer.

TEXT sets current text printing mode on the printer by the width, height and shade of character.

TPRINT: As *GPRINT but string is made up of normal characters, i.e. a large E would be constructed with lots of smaller Es.

ULOAD: Loads set of previously saved user-definable characters.

UNDERLINE: Turns printer underlining facility ON or OFF.

USAVE: Saves user definable characters.

WINDOW: Allows graphics window to be defined by controlling size of 'box' on screen.

WVALS: Prints co-ordinates or current graphics window.

The majority of commands will work on the Epson printers FX80, RX80, MX100 and MX80, though some commands will not work on some of the models.

Disc Doctor

If you own a disc drive then this type of utility can be a life-saver – an essential programming aid in my opinion – and they don't come much better than this one from Computer Concepts.

In addition to providing direct disc editing and facilities for recovering data from corrupted discs, other general utilities are provided. The complete list of commands and their operations are as follows:

DIS is a full 6502 disassembler including an offset disassembly option.

DISCTAPE transfers a program from disc to tape.

DOWNLOAD loads a program from disc and then relocates it at the specified address.

DSEARCH allows a specified string to be sought on a disc.

DZAP invokes an interactive disc editor.

EDIT displays function key definitions.

FIND searches a BASIC program for occurrences of a specified string, listing the line numbers where string is found.

```
DISC DOCTOR 1.09
    DIS ((sta)) ((end)) ((ofs))
    DISCTAPE (afsp) ((afsp))...
    DOWNLOAD (fsp) ((adr))
    DSEARCH (str) (trk) ((trk)(sct)(drv))
    DZAP ((trk)) ((trk)(sct)(drv))
    EDIT ((key no.))
    FIND (str)
    FORM (drv) (no. trks) ((stt)) ((S))
    JOIN (fsp) (afsp) ((afsp))...
    MENU ((drv))
    MOVE ((dest page)) ((src page))
    MSEARCH (str) ((adr))
    MZAP ((adr))
    PARTLOAD (fsp) (ofs) (ext) (adr)
    RECOVER (trk) (sct) (sct) (adr) (drv)
    RESTORE (trk) (sct) (sct) (adr) (drv)
    SHIFT (src) (dest) (ext)
    SWAP ((drv))
    TAPEDISC ((fsp))...
    VERIFY ((drv)) ((no. trks)) ((stt))
OS 1.20
```

Fig. 13.11. Disc Doctor help sheet.

*FORM formats all or part of a disc. Any special, alternative disc catalogue may be formatted thereby allowing up to 60 files per disc.

*JOIN joins files together as specified to form a single file. Initial files are left intact.

*MENU displays menu of programs in special file on disc.

*MOVE relocates a BASIC program in memory.

*MSEARCH searches memory for specified string.

*MZAP invokes the interactive memory editor.

*PARTLOAD loads any part of a long file.

*RECOVER loads specified sectors from a disc into memory.

*RESTORE saves specified sectors onto disc from memory.

*SHIFT shifts a block of memory.

*SWAP swaps to alternative disc catalogue.

*TAPEDISK transfers a program from disc to tape.

*VERIFY verifies that a disc has been formatted correctly.

MUROM

MUROM is a sound extension ROM from Beebug. Tunes and sounds may be created using the channel editor or by using the Beeb's keyboard as a simulated piano keyboard.

The MUROM command summary is as follows:

*PLAY initialises the variable speed, interrupt-driven playback routine.

*DISP displays the tune playing in MODE 7.

TEMPO allows tempo of tune to be altered.

KEYB sets BBC keyboard to act as piano keyboard.

SCORE invokes full screen music editor.

ENVLP invokes the sound envelope editor.

TRANS transposes up or down by a number of semitones.

MONOC disables colour output to aid readability on black and white screens.

MUROM also contains ten predefined envelopes that will set up particular instruments such as *FLUTE and *SYNTH. Ten effects envelopes are also included such as *ZAP, *EXPLODE and *SIREN. When in the music editor, eight sub-commands are available, and these are:

MODE selects channel editing sequence.

GO moves to any note in score.

PLAY enables single stepping of music.

OCTV changes octave of any channel.

ENVL changes envelope of any channel.

LOAD loads music.

SAVE saves music.

KEY toggles between note name and keyboard position.

Music and sound sequences may be incorporated in programs and used with or without the MUROM present.

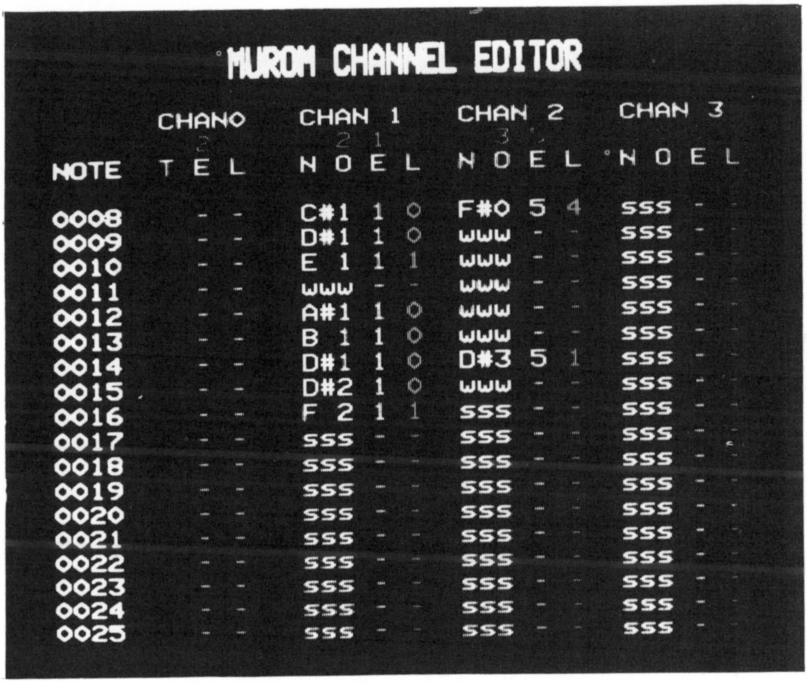

Fig. 13.12. The MUROM channel editor.

HELP ROM

This 8K ROM from Beebug provides details on just about everything you will need to know. Over 18000 characters of text have been squashed into it providing information on:

BASIC keywords
SOUND
COLOUR
TELETEXT
VDU commands
FX calls

If, for instance, you wish to know the colour codes for magenta, you would simply type:

    *H MAGENTA

and the reply would be:

    MAGENTA frgd 4, bkgd 132

Figure 13.13 shows a typical screen response to the commands *H SOUND and *H FX5.

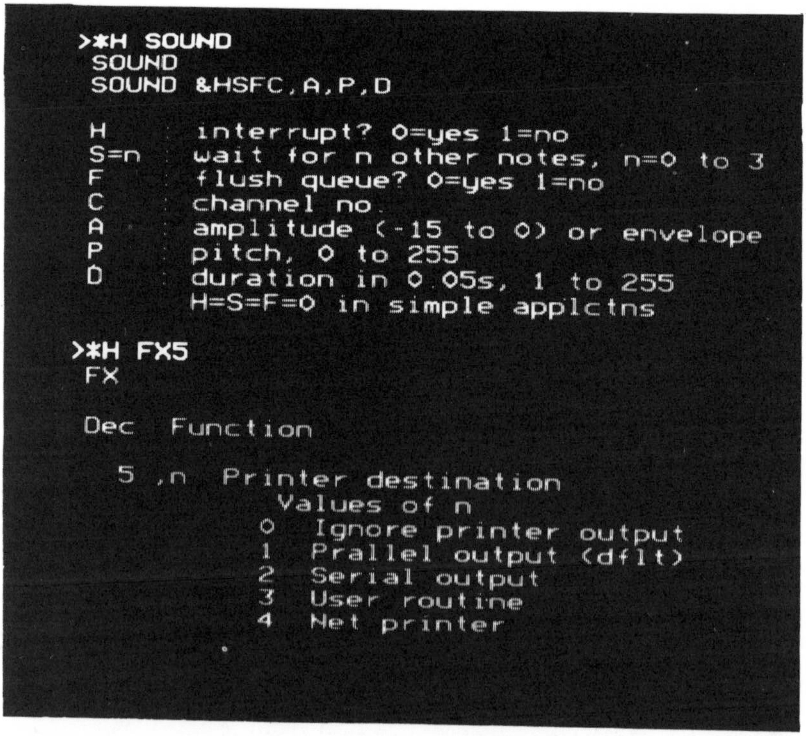

```
>*H SOUND
 SOUND
 SOUND &HSFC,A,P,D

 H        interrupt? 0=yes 1=no
 S=n      wait for n other notes, n=0 to 3
 F        flush queue? 0=yes 1=no
 C        channel no.
 A        amplitude (-15 to 0) or envelope
 P        pitch, 0 to 255
 D        duration in 0.05s, 1 to 255
          H=S=F=0 in simple applctns

>*H FX5
 FX

 Dec  Function

     5 ,n  Printer destination
              Values of n
           0   Ignore printer output
           1   Prallel output (dflt)
           2   Serial output
           3   User routine
           4   Net printer
```

Fig. 13.13. The HELP ROM in action.

Appendix A
Converting BASIC I to BASIC II

BASIC II provides several enhancements over its predecessor BASIC I. The most useful of these are the EQU functions which are implemented as pseudo-opcodes. These functions and their operations are:

EQUB : assemble specified byte
EQUW : assemble specified word (2 bytes)
EQUD : assemble specified double word (4 bytes)
EQUS : assemble specified string as ASCII characters

Numerous programs in the Portfolio take advantage of these commands, which would therefore make them inoperable on Beebs with BASIC I. These commands can be simulated quite simply using the ability of the FN command.

Program A.1 lists the function definitions plus a suitable demonstration.

```
 10 REM ** SIMULATING BASIC II EQU **
 20 P%=&900
 30 [
 40              LDA #255
 50              OPT FNequs("TEST",3)
 60              LDX #0
 70              OPT FNequb(6,3)
 80              LDY #&33
 90              OPT FNequw(&FFFF,3)
100              STX &70
110              OPT FNequd(&12345678,3)
120              LDX #&AA
130              RTS
140 ]
150 END
160 :
500 DEF FNequs(string$,opt)
510 $P%=string$
520 P%=P%+LEN(string$)
530 =opt
540 :
550 DEF FNequb(byte%,opt)
560 ?P%=byte%
570 P%=P%+1
```

```
580 =opt
590 :
600 DEF FNequw(word%,opt)
610 ?P%=word% MOD 256
620 P%?1=word% DIV 256
630 P%=P%+2
640 =opt
650 :
660 DEF FNequd(double%,opt)
670 !P%=double%
680 P%=P%+4
690 =opt
```

Program A.1. Simulating the BASIC II EQU functions in BASIC I.

Taking each definition as it appears in the program, FNequs (lines 500 to 530) uses the program counter variable P% as the string argument for the ASCII character string passed into the function via 'string$'. Before exit, P% is incremented by the length of the string.

FNequb (lines 550 to 580) takes the value 'byte%' and simply pokes it into memory at P%. The program counter is incremented by one and completes. FNequw (lines 600 to 640) is an extension and provides two pokes at the position of P%. The high and low bytes are extracted from 'word' using the MOD and DIV operators. Finally, FNequd (lines 660 to 690) uses the word indirection operator to pling its four bytes into memory.

The assembler text (lines 40 to 130) shows how each procedure should be called. The second parameter in each of the OPT FN calls (3 throughout) simply refers to the OPT selection and this should be seeded as required by the program. To end with, Figure A.1 shows the assembler listing provided when running this program, while the hex dump in Figure A.2 shows that each FN has indeed performed the required task.

```
>RUN
0900
0900 A9 FF    LDA #255
0906          OPT FNequs("TEST",3)
0906 A2 00    LDX #0
0909          OPT FNequb(6,3)
0909 A0 33    LDY #&33
090D          OPT FNequw(&FFFF,3)
090D 86 70    STX &70
0913          OPT FNequd(&12345678,3)
0913 A2 AA    LDX #&AA
0915 60       RTS
```

Fig. A.1. Assembler listing produced by Program A.1.

900	A9
901	FF
902	54
903	45
904	53
905	54
906	A2
907	0
908	6
909	A0
90A	33
90B	FF
90C	FF
90D	86
90E	70
90F	78
910	56
911	34
912	12
913	A2
914	AA
915	60

Fig. A.2. A hex dump of the code assembled by Program A.1, showing that the functions have worked.

Appendix B
ROM Book Programs in Bar Code Form

This appendix contains some of the longer programs in this book in bar code form. Owners of the MEP bar code reader will be able to read these directly into the Beeb following the instructions in the Bar Code Reader Handbook.

Full details of the MEP bar code reader can be obtained from:

Micro Electronics Education Program
Cheviot House
Coach Lane Campus
Newcastle-upon Tyne NE7 7XA

Because of the space requirements needed to reproduce bar code listings, and to make the programs easier and quicker to read in, each of the programs has been extensively compacted to exclude REMs, excess spaces and to utilise multi-statement lines, though this will not affect the overall functioning of the programs.

The numbers that appear within the bar code listings to the left relate to the current line number in the program and should not be entered from the keyboard – the bar code reader will extract this from the bar codes.

The programs presented are:

Program 5.1:   The ROM Image Formatter. (p. 207)
Program 8.2:   The BRK Interpreter. (p. 220)
Program 9.2:   Implementing *HELP BTOOL. (p. 229)
Program 9.3:   Testing the command table. (p. 233)
Program 9.4:   The Complete BASIC Tools Sideways ROM interpreter. (p. 240)
Program 9.12:   Implementing a language ROM. (p. 261)
Program 10.1:   Sideways ROM menu. (p. 274)

Program 5.1: The ROM Image Formatter

10
70

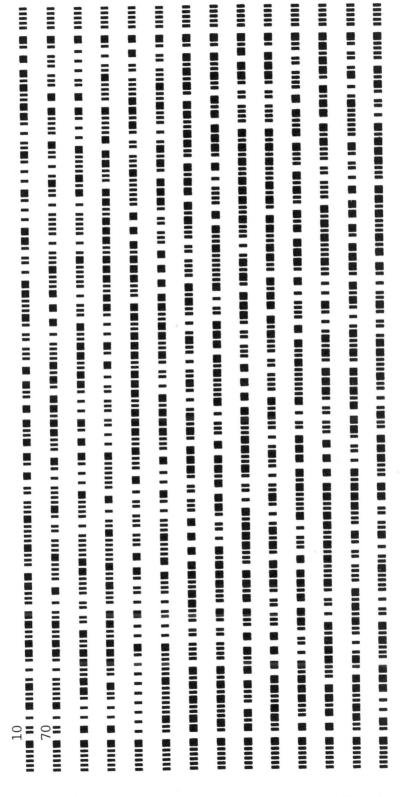

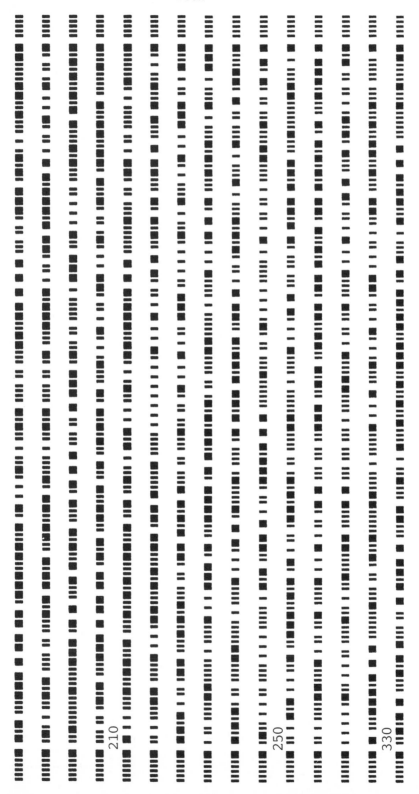

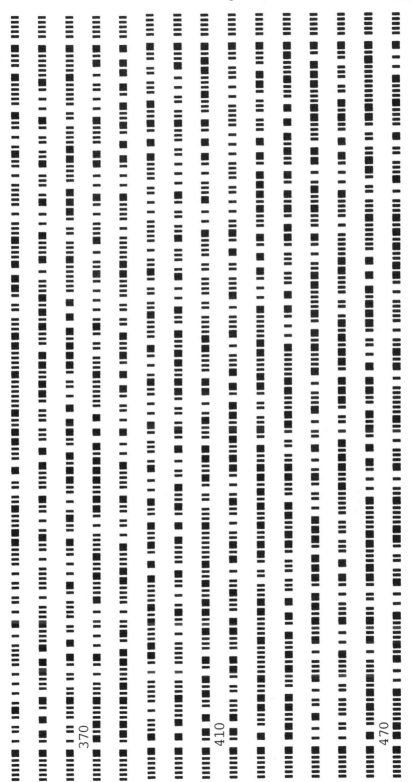

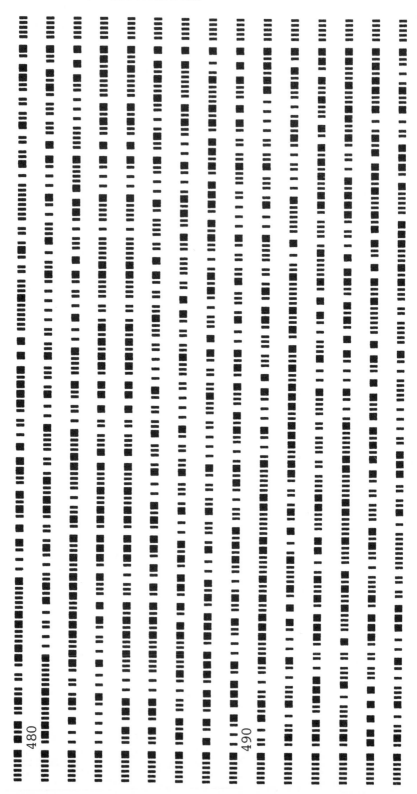

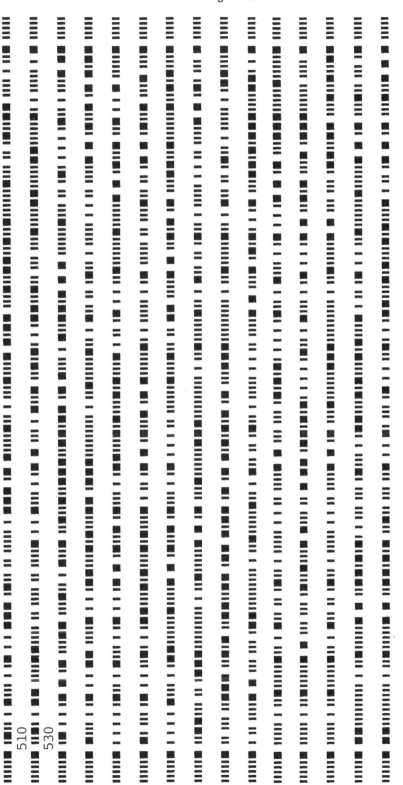

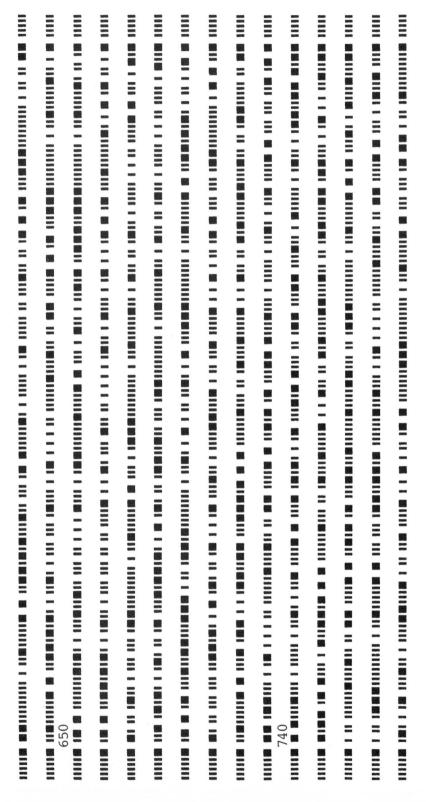

870

940

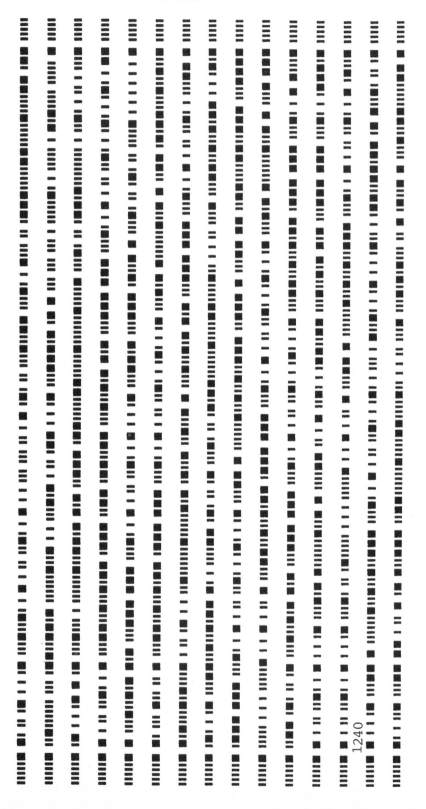

1240

1340

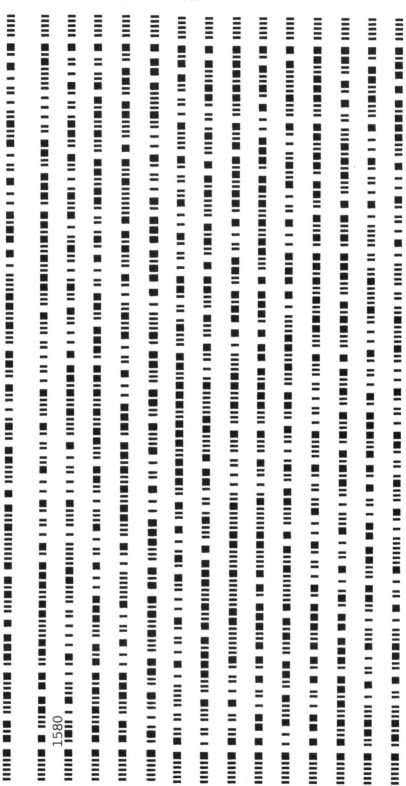

1930

1960 1980

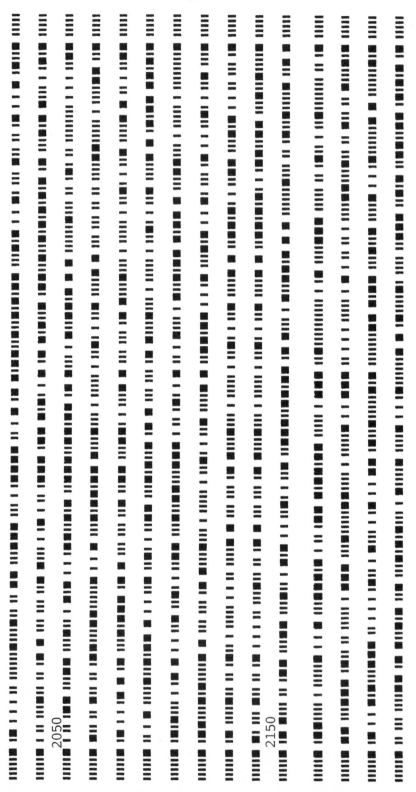

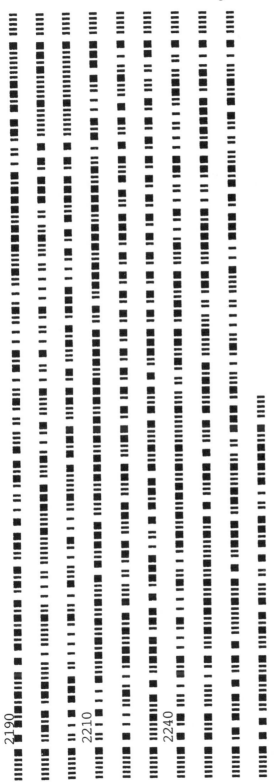

Program 8.2: The BRK Interpreter

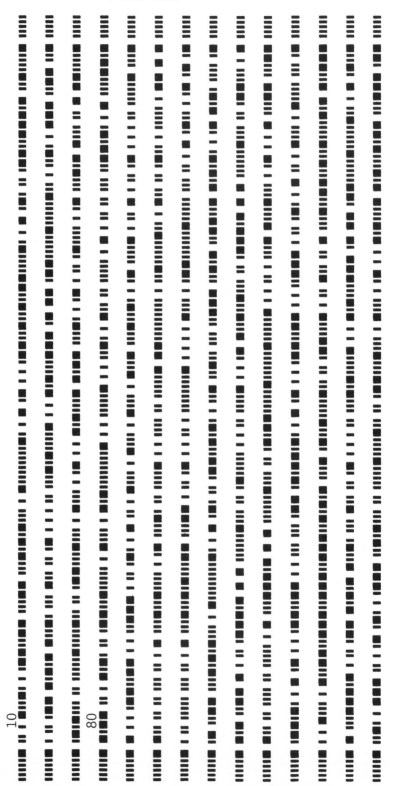

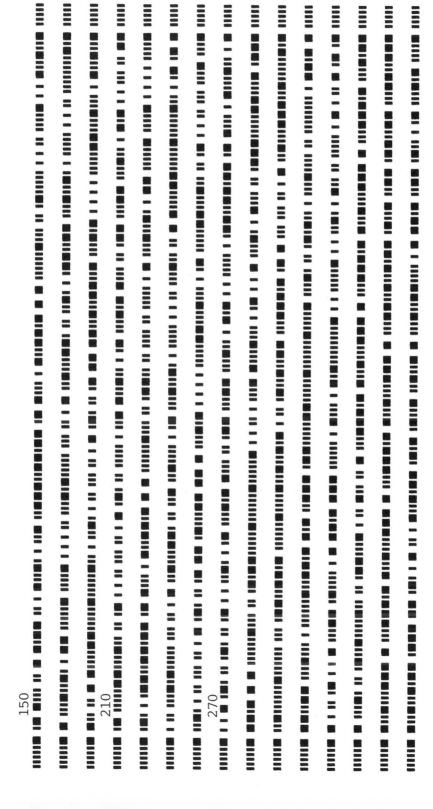

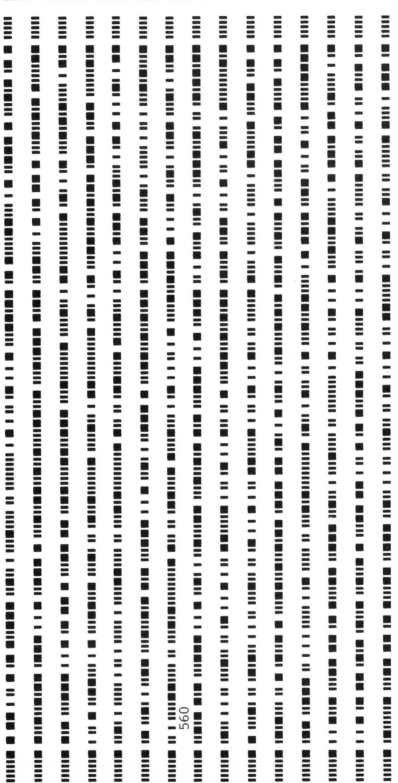

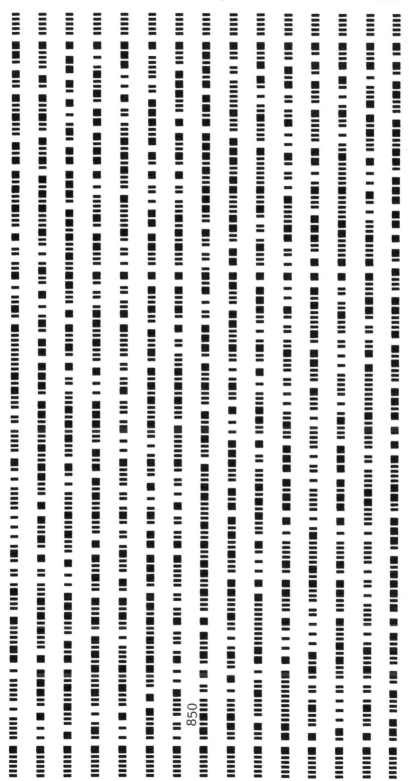

850

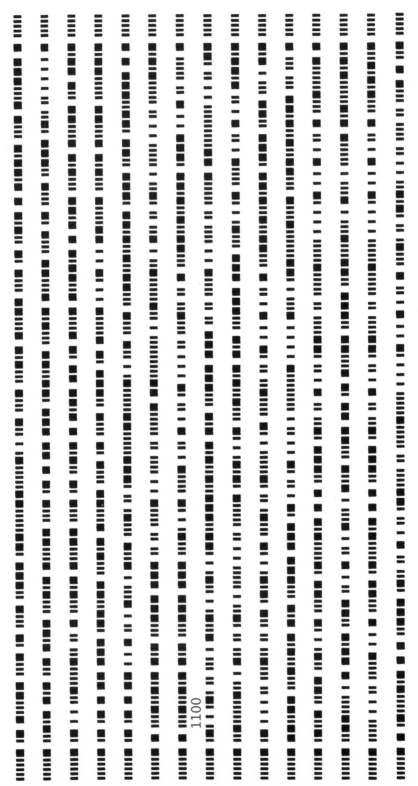

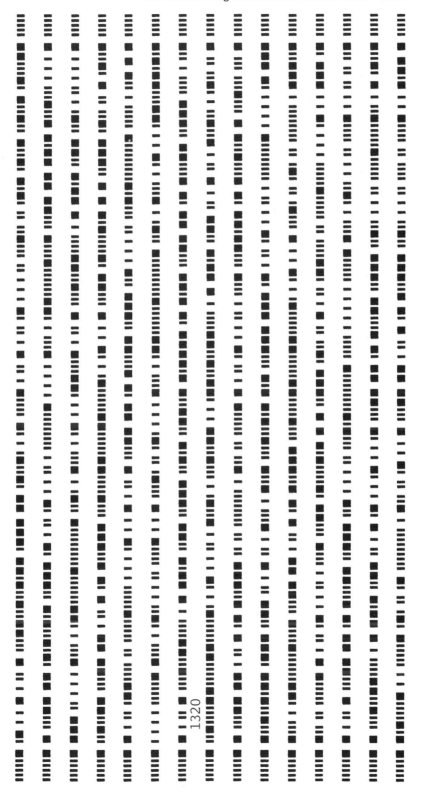

1320

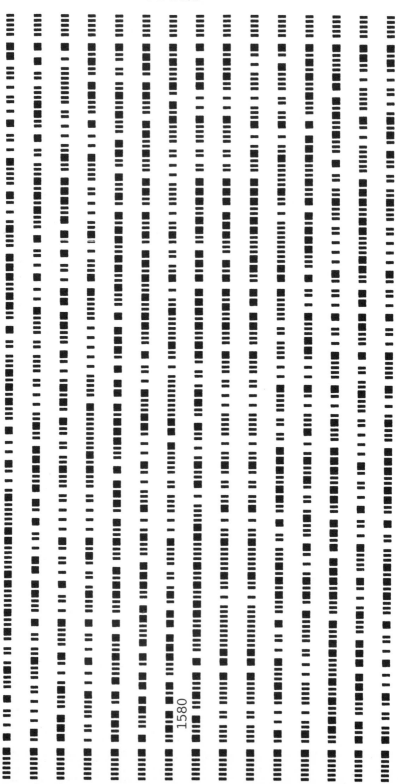

1800

Program 9.2: Implementing *HELP BTOOL

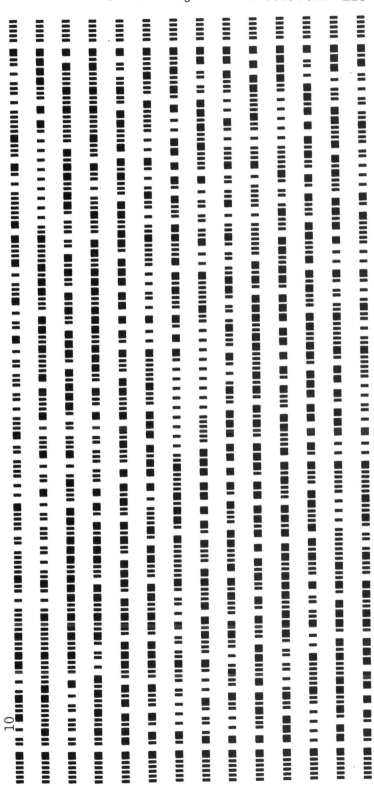

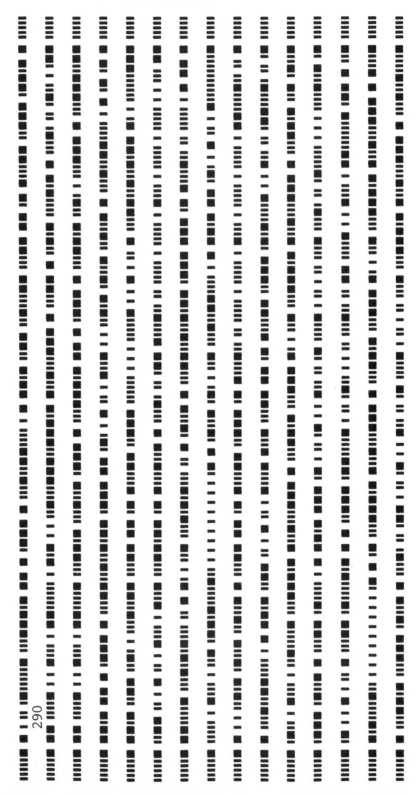

640

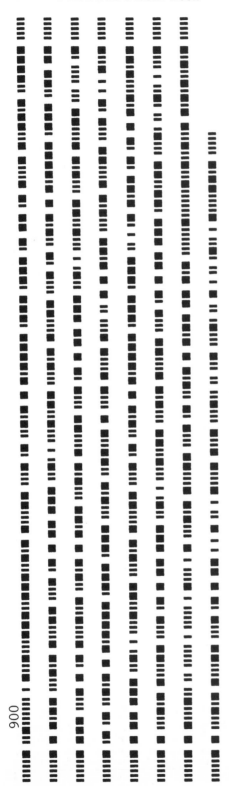

900

Program 9.3: Testing the command table

10

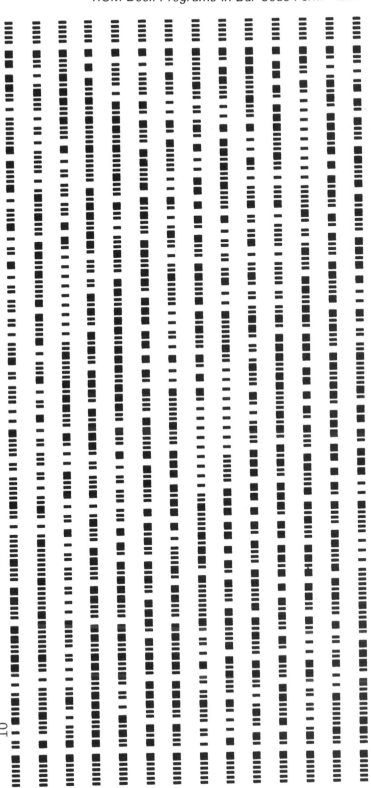

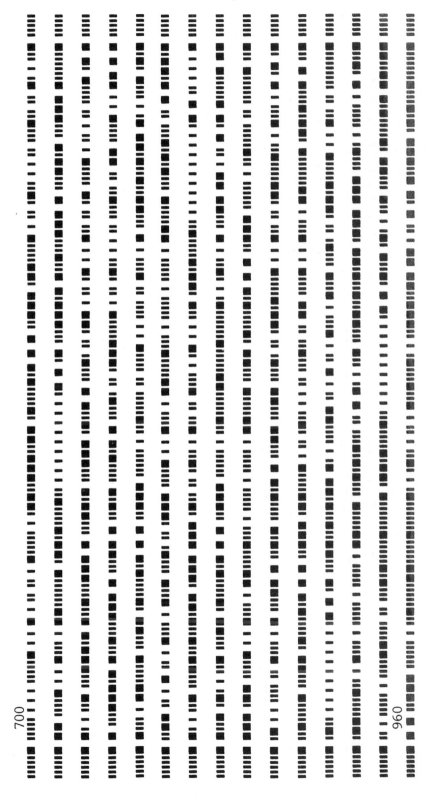

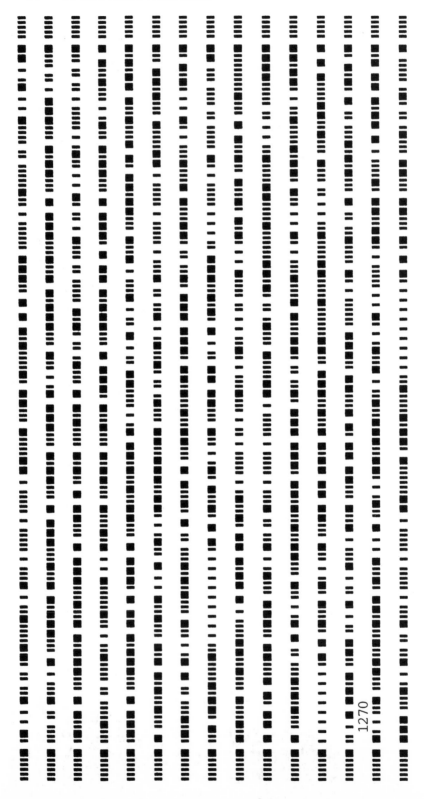

1270

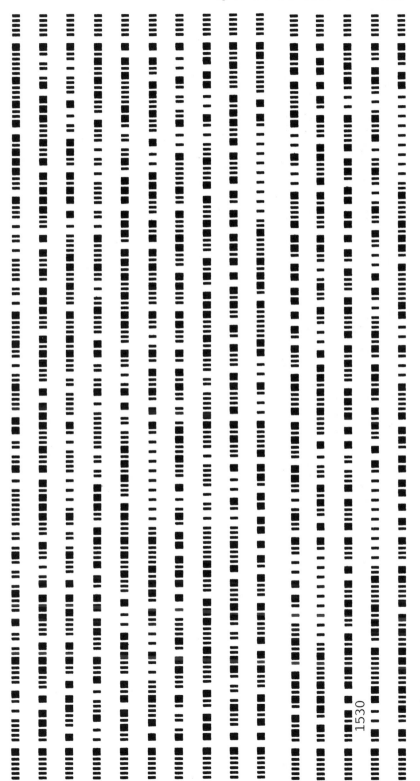

1530

1730 1740

Program 9.4: The Complete BASIC Tools Sideways ROM Interpreter

10

270

540

840

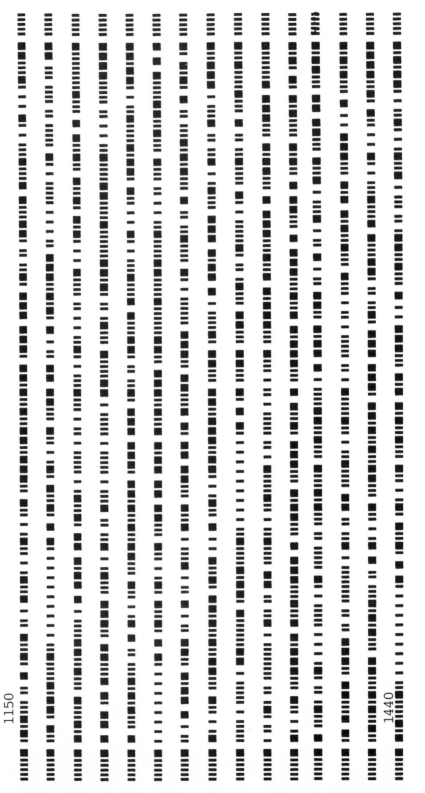

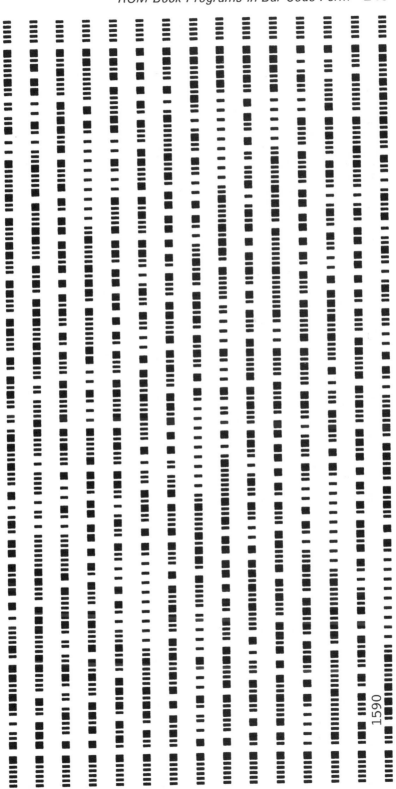

1590

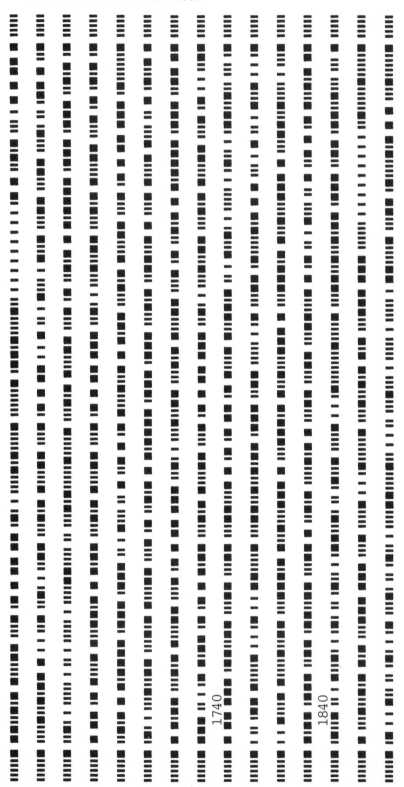

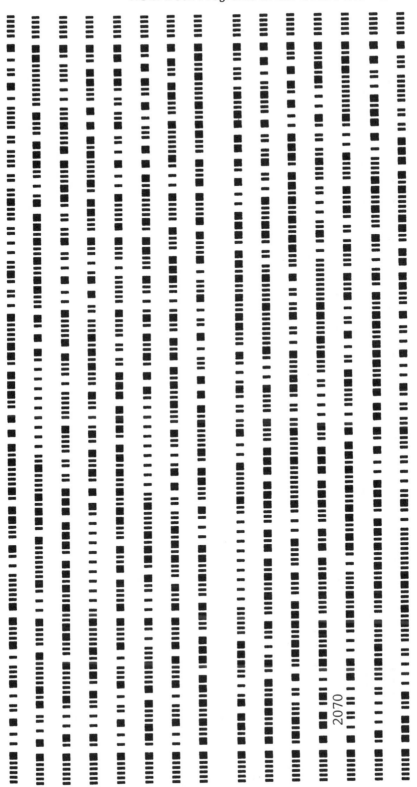

2070

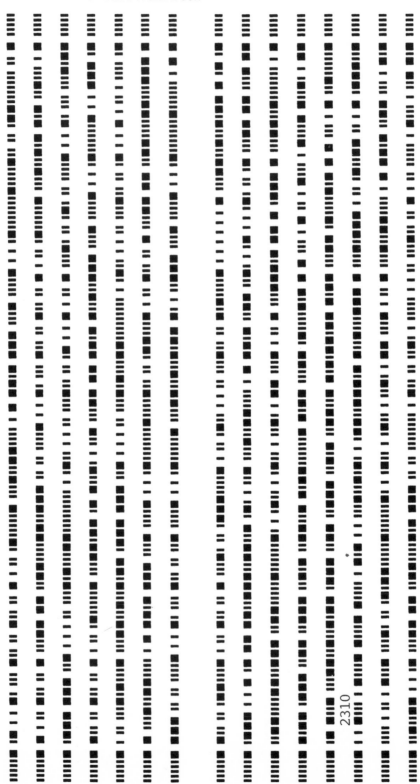

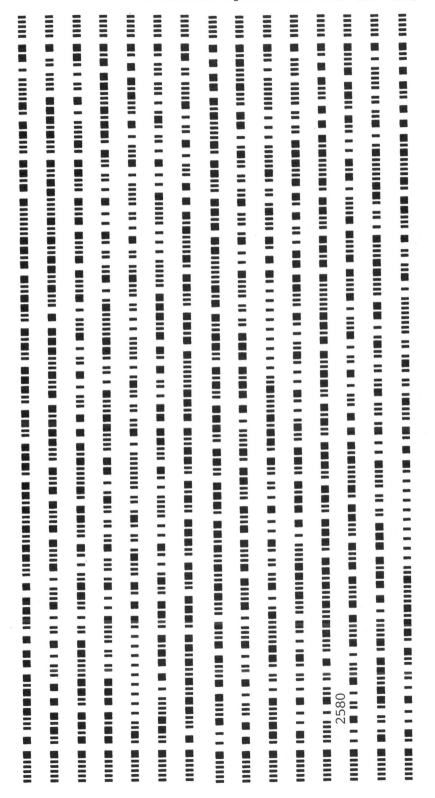

2580

2820

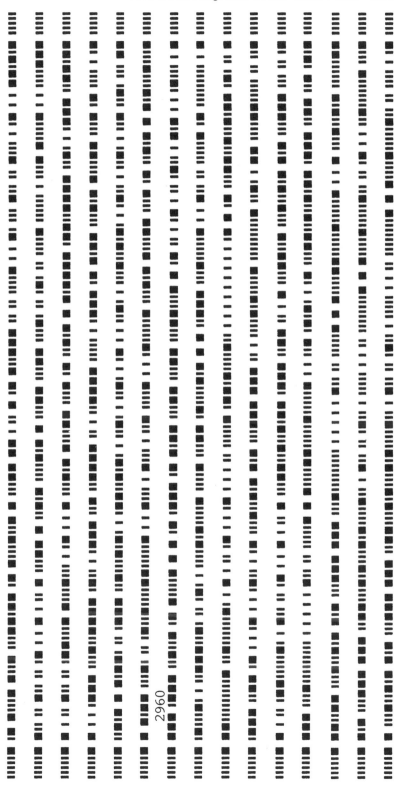

2960

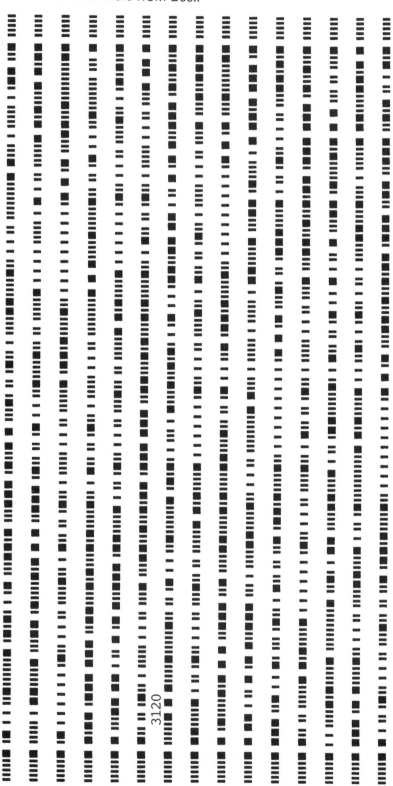

3120

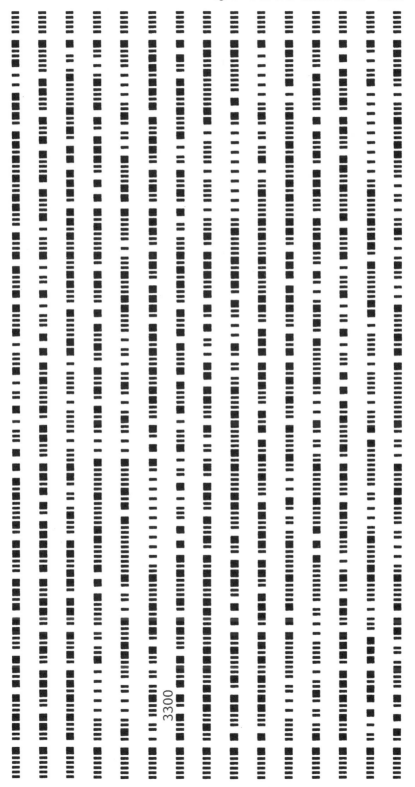

3300

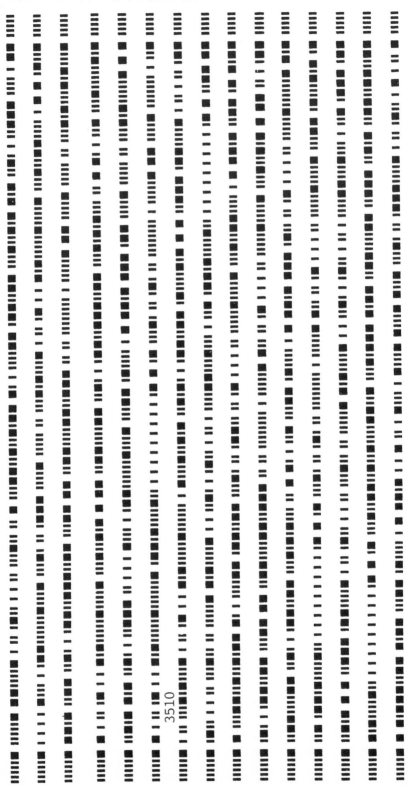

3510

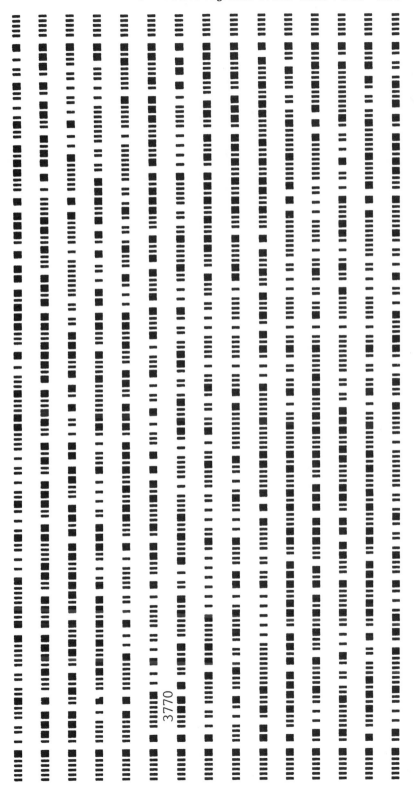

3770

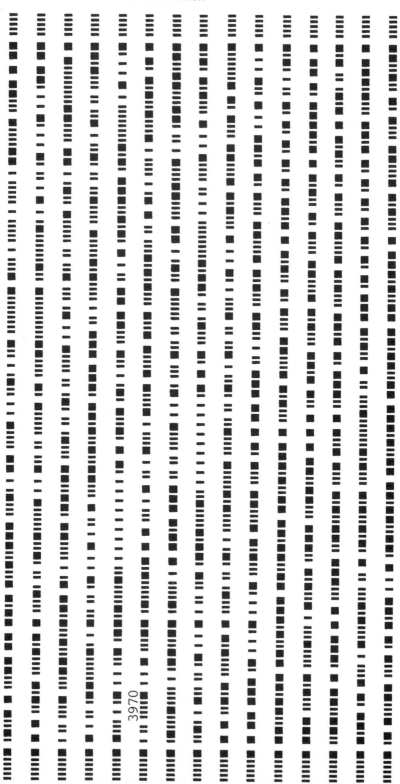

4200

4280

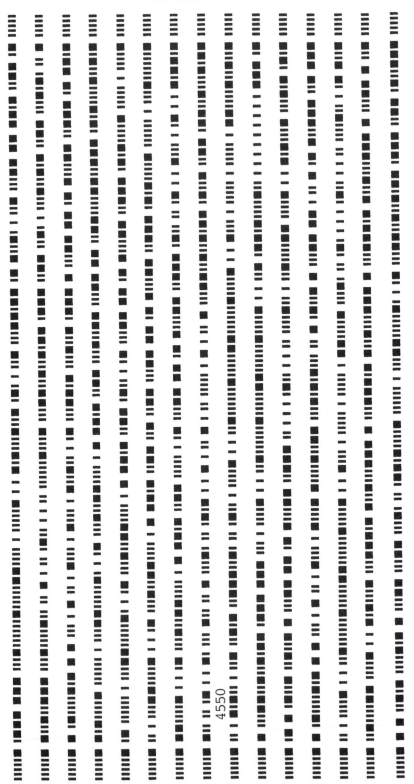

4790

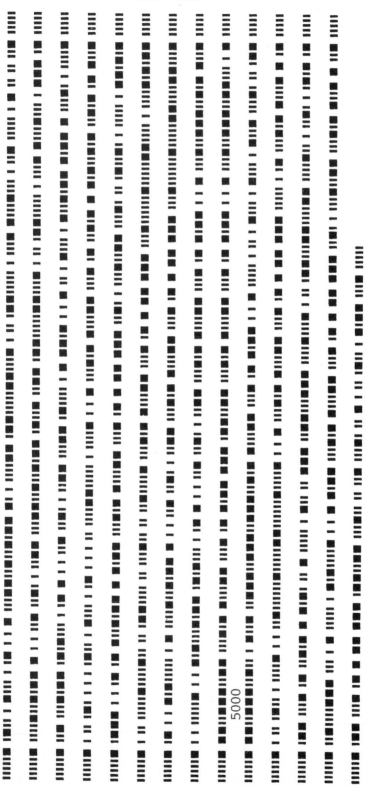

Program 9.12: Implementing a language ROM

10

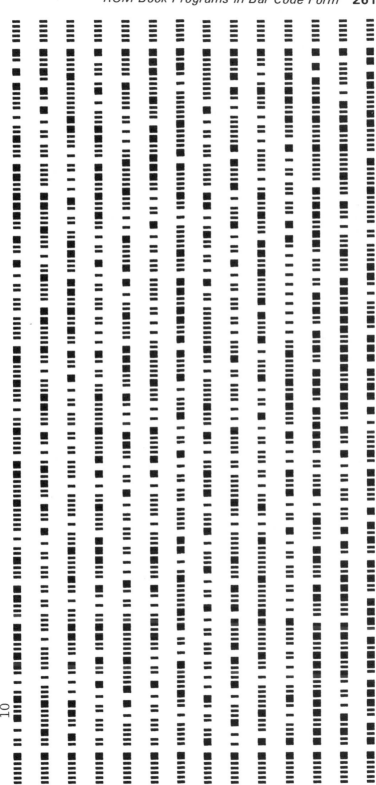

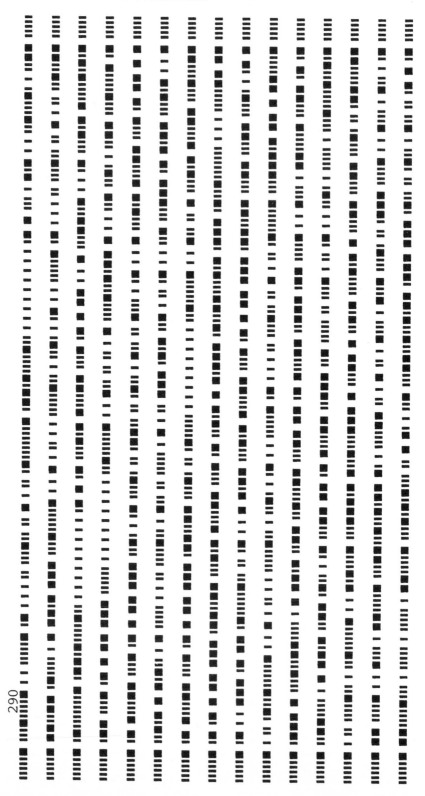

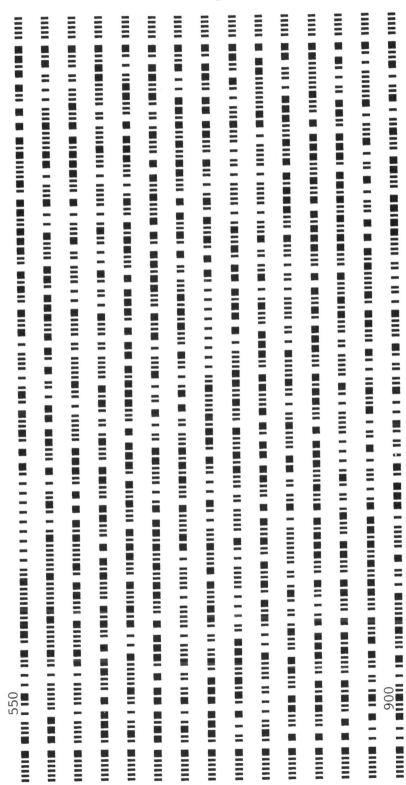

550

900

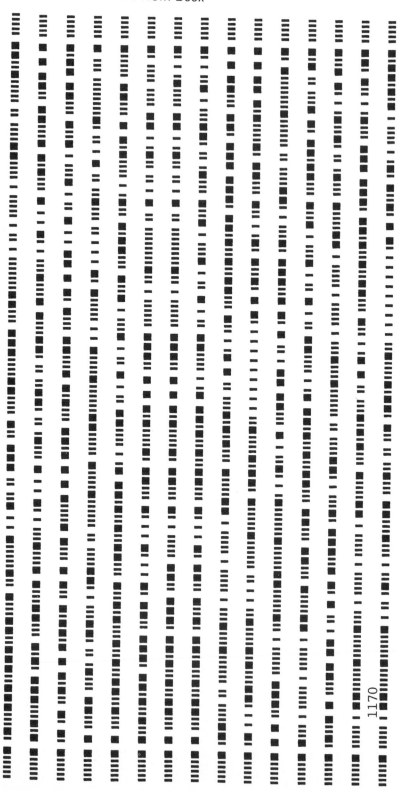

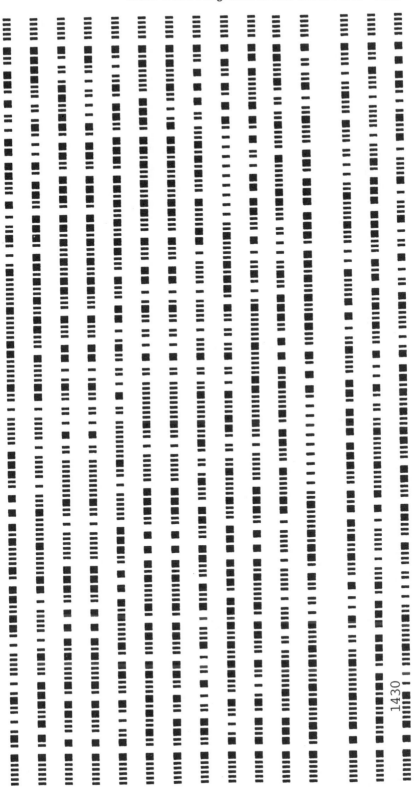

1430

1690

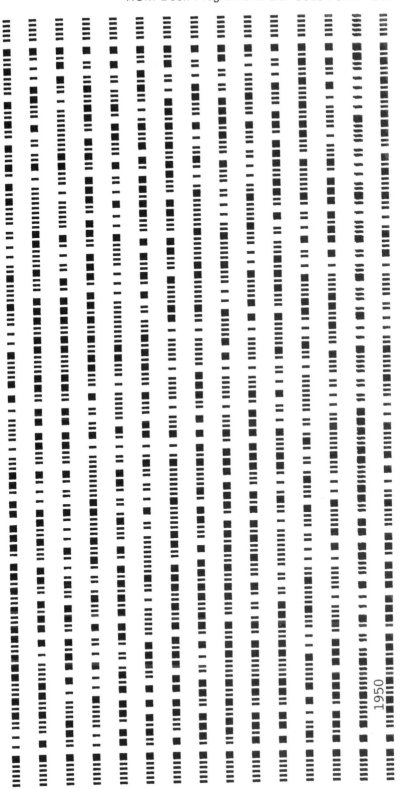

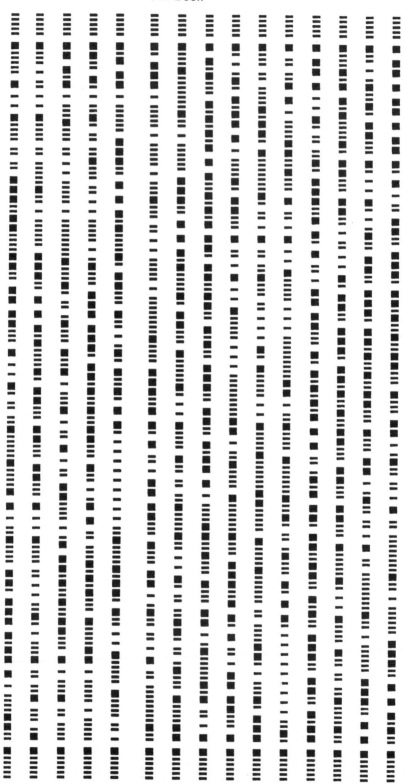

2190

2440

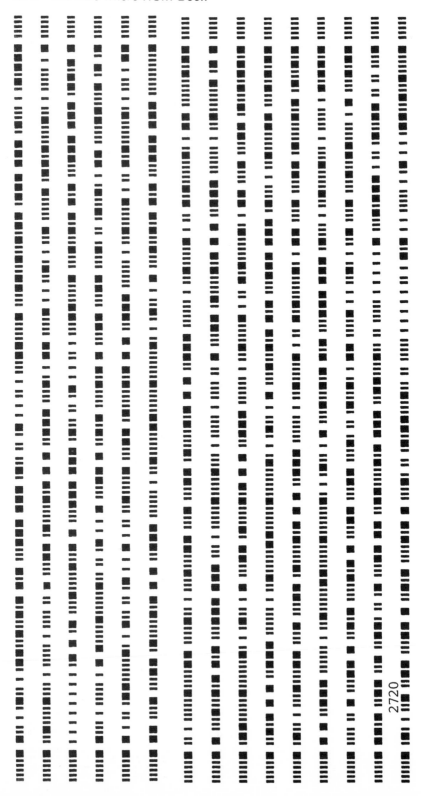

2720

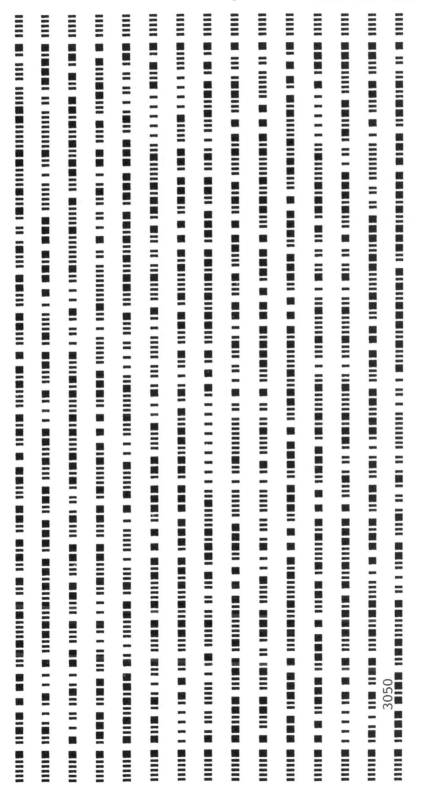

3050

3270

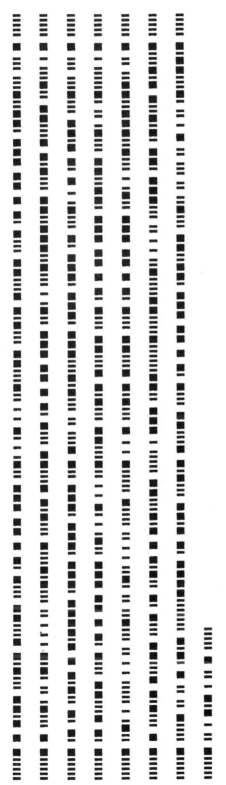

Program 10.1: Sideways ROM menu

10

120

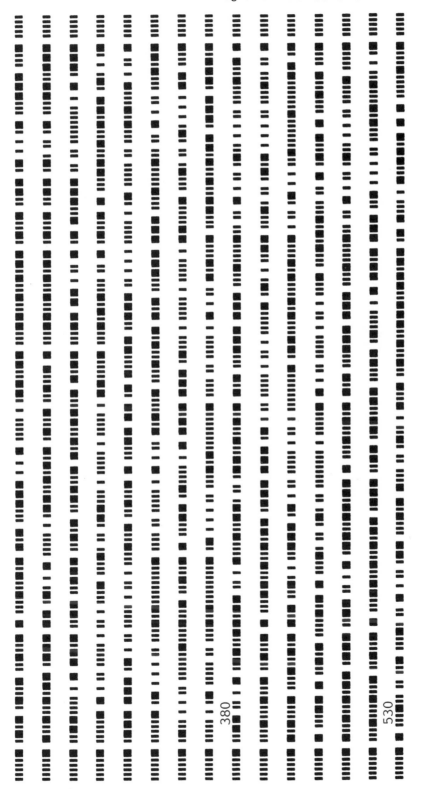

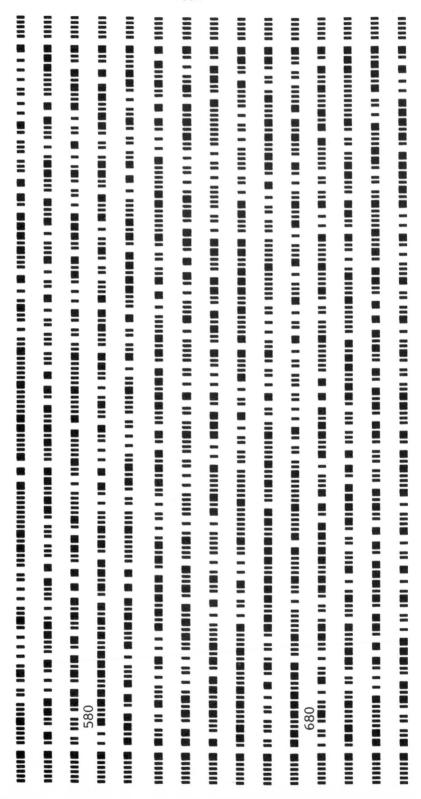

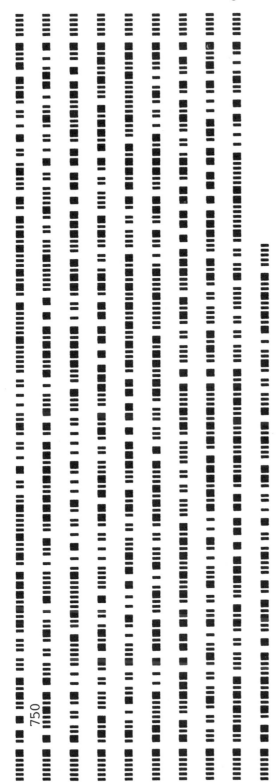

750

Appendix C
Useful Addresses

APTL
Station Road
Clowne
Chesterfield S43 4AB
Product: ROM expansion board

Aries Computers
Science Park
Milton Road
Cambridge CB4 4BH
Product: ROM expansion board

Beebugsoft
Mailing Dept.
PO BOX 109
High Wycombe
Bucks
Products: ROM firmware

Computer Concepts
Gaddesden Place
Hemel Hempstead
Herts HP2 6EX
Products: ROM firmware and
ROM expansion board

Digital Services
Fitzherbert Road
Farlington
Portsmouth
Hants PO6 1UR
Products: ROM firmware

HCR Electronics
Industrial Unit, Parker Road
Chelmsford
Essex CM2 0ES
Products: Eprom programmer and
ROM expansion board

Micro Power
Northwood House
North Street
Leeds LS7 2AA
Products: ROM firmware

Mirra Systems
26 Spicer Place
Rugby
Warwickshire CV22 7EA
Products: ROM firmware

Northern Computers
Churchfield Road
Frodsham
Cheshire WA6 6RD
Product: External ROM expansion
board

Solidisk Technology Ltd
17 Sweyne Avenue
Southend-on-Sea
Essex SS2 6JQ
Products: Sideways RAM; Eprom
programmers and erasers

System
12 Collegiate Crescent
Sheffield S10 2BA
Products: ROM firmware

Viglen Computer Supplies
Unit 7
Trumpers Way
Hanwell
London W7 2QA
Product: ROM cartridges

Vine Micros
Marshborough
Nr. Sandwich
Kent CT13 0PG
Products: ROM firmware

Index

ADE, 190
ADDCOMM, 85, 86, 87, 88, 178
APTL ROM board, 149
ARIES B12 ROM board, 148
auto boot, 23, 24, 127, 128

BASIC Extensions, 185
BASIC I to BASIC II, 203
BEEP, 89, 97
BRK, 12, 25, 84
BRK interpreter, 88–96

CARETAKER, 180
command table, 110
copyright, 13
copyright offset pointer, 13, 17

DEBUG, 191
Disc Doctor, 199
DIY EPROM programmer, 164
DIY extension socket, 152

EPROM, 5
EPROM erasers, 177
EPROM programmers, 163–77
EXMON, 192
Exprom ROM board, 150
extended vector space, 60
extended vectors, 59, 60

filing systems, see ROM filing system
FNKEY, 97
FX calls, 9, 11, 12

Graphics Extension ROM, 196
Gremlin, 193

header, 13
HELP, 27, 28, 29, 99–105
HELP ROM, 202

IC, 3
information table, 12
internal key codes, 129
Interpreter, 195
interpreter, BRK, 88–96
  TOOLKIT, 63–84
  writing and testing, 106–24
IRQ, 25

language entry point, 13, 15, 33
language – Monitor TREK, 136–44
language ROMs, 11, 12, 33–36

language workspace, 34

machine code monitors, 189
memory usage, 9
Micro Pulse ROM box, 150
MUROM, 200

NMI, 29, 30, 31

OSBYTE, 9, 11, 12, 26, 134, 135
OSRDRM, 9
OSWORD, 27, 130–34

PACK, 89
pointer table, 11
Printmaster, 198

ROM, 5
  anatomy, 5, 6
  auto-boot, 23, 24, 127–30
  boards, 145
    choosing, 146–8
  BRK, 25
  copyright, 13
  copyright offset pointer, 13, 17
  disabler, 160
  extended vectors, see vectors
  filing system, 2, 11, 31, 37–58
    hash headers, 58
    header, 38
    image, 41, 43
    service coding, 39–41
  fitting, 4
  header, 13
  HELP, 27, 28, 29, 99–105
  information table, 12
  IRQ, 25
  language current, 12
  language entry point, 13, 15, 33
  language workspace, 34
  languages, 11, 136–44
  memory map, 1
  menu, 156
  NMI, 29, 30, 31
  OSBYTE, 26, 134, 135
  OSWORD, 27, 130–34
  paging system, 1–18
  pointer table, 11
  positions, 2
  priority, 3, 6
  removal, 4, 6
  service, 19
  service calls, 20–32
  service entry point, 13, 15
  service requests, 11, 19
  title, 17
  Tube relocation, 13, 18
  type, 13, 14, 15

unrecognised command, 24
vectors, 43, 59–61
version number, 17
workspace, 21, 22, 23
workspace absolute, 22
workspace claim, 21, 29
workspace private, 21, 22, 23, 126, 127

SCREEN, 97
service call 0, 20, 21
service call 1, 21, 124, 125
service call 2, 21, 22, 23
service call 3, 23, 24
service call 4, 24, 106–24
service call 5, 25
service call 6, 25
service call 7, 26
service call 8, 27, 130
service call 9, 27, 28, 97–105, 135
service call 10, 29
service call 11, 29, 30
service call 12, 30, 31
service call 13, 31, 38
service call 14, 31, 38, 39
service call 15, 31
service call 16, 31
service call 17, 31
service call 18, 32
service call 254, 32
service call 255, 32
service entry point, 13, 15
service requests, 11, 19
service ROMs, 19–32
sideways RAM, 98, 154
sideways ROM sockets, 3
SLEUTH, 187
Solidisk, 155

TEST, 89
title string, 17, 124, 125
TOOLKIT, 182
TOOLKIT Interpreter, 62–84
Tube, 32, 35, 36
Tube relocation, 13, 18
type, 13, 15
type table, 14

U TOOLS, 184
unrecognised command, 24

VDU, 97
vectors, 43, 59–61
  extended vectors, 59, 60
Viglen ROM cartridge, 151

workspace,
  absolute, 22
  claim, 21, 22, 29
  private, 21, 22, 126, 127